Complete
Weight Training
Book

by Bill Reynolds

Cover design by Mark Cowans
Photos by Bill Reynolds

© 1976 by
World Publications
P.O. Box 366, Mountain View, CA 94040

Second Printing, November 1976

Library of Congress Catalog Number 75-32443
ISBN 0-89037-110-5

CONTENTS

INTRODUCTION

If someone had told me five years ago that I would write a book about weight training, I'd have been a bit amused. The activity was a joy to me, and I was teaching it regularly at the University of Washington . . . but write a book?

In reality, however, the seed for what you hold in your hands was planted that long ago in my weight training classes. It very quickly became apparent to me that a huge amount of misinformation about weight training was circulating among my students. At times it was a trial to convince them that they were going down a blind alley that I had explored years before. I tried all the weight training books available in an attempt to remedy this problem, but they were either outdated or downright misleading. None of the authors I read, for example, thought much of women training with weights.

Over a two-year period, I gradually evolved a set of 25 handouts that served as my class text. To a man (er . . . woman), my students were enthusiastic about the handout series, and many commented that it should be published. My ego made me easy to convince, so I sat down and began writing this book.

How you use *The Complete Weight Training Book* depends largely on your degree of experience with weights. Beginners should start at page one and read through page 42 before touching a weight. From there, it's a matter of choosing an appropriate training schedule from one of the subsequent chamters, looking up the exercises in the excercise pool chapter, and having at it.

Intermediates and advanced individuals will, in all likelihood, already be well grounded in how to do the exercises. They should benefit from a review of the basic chapters, but will receive the most assistance from the programs I've outlined in chapters four, five and six. Each of these schedules was formulated only after consulting an expert in each area. As an example, the section on gymnastics was written after a discussion with Sho Fukushima, Danish Olympic gymnastics coach.

There are hundreds of people to thank for helping me along the way. Dwight Hawkes, my high school football and baseball coach, started me in weight training, and Mike Kesl got me hooked. Meridy Schmidt, Marla Koss, and especially Sally McQuillen gave me a greater appreciation of women in the weight room. Sally gave me more of her time—both in consultation and in posing for exercise illustrations—than any person could ask.

The models for exercise photos were Sally, Bill Perales, Sandy and Mike Bassoni, Danny Waller, Jim Dahl, Donna Valaitis, Marie Johnson, John Powell, Brent and Ann Turner, Al Feuerbach, Ray Leso, Roger Quinn, Blair Kephart, John Raffaele, Dale Adrian, Pat Neve, Al Jones, Paul Love, Meridy Schmidt, Charles Glass, Eddie Rulie, Ann Block, Neil Darrow, Casey Donovan and Marlene Carlson. Special thanks to Steve Reeves for permission to reprint his photo. With the exception of pages 162 and 198, all photos are by the author. The photos were taken at the European Health Spa (Mountain View), Johnny's Gym (Alameda), Berkeley YMCA, University of California (Berkeley), and De Anza College (Cupertino).

Eric Hughes, Mollie Tyson, John C. Grimek, Eric Evans and Dale Adrian read rough copies of the book and made valuable comments. Dave Prokop, my editor, improved the basic text far more than I would care to admit. We worked like a well-oiled team, and any literary quality that seeps through is a credit to him. And if you like the way the book looks, that's Virginia Bennett's contribution. She did all of the layout work.

To everyone who has helped, thanks, I couldn't have done it without you.

Bill Reynolds
Mountain View, California

1

What's It All About?

The first known weight-trained individual in history was Milo of Crotona, a Greek wrestler in the ancient days when bouts occasionally ended with one competitor dead. Not wishing to suffer such a permanent penalty, Milo determined to make himself the strongest and most physically fit wrestler in all of Greece. The training approach he chose was to daily lift a young calf across his shoulders and walk around a large stadium bearing the extra weight. Naturally, as the bullock grew older and heavier, Milo grew more powerful until he was acknowledged as the strongest man in the ancient world. For 24 years he was invincible in the wrestling arena. During that period, he was champion six consecutive times at the Olympic Games, 10 times at Isthmia, nine at Nemea and seven at Delphi.

Milo's strength-building system was a crude form of progressive resistance exercise, or what we now call weight training. Thousands of Milo's modern day successors now walk the earth. They are men, women and children who have recognized that training with barbells, dumbells and other heavy apparatus quickly enhances performances in their chosen sports, improves physical appearance, and is a shortcut to physical fitness.

It is probably safe to say that there are no sports today that do not boast of weight-trained athletes. Even distance runners and others to whom economy of bodyweight is vitally important have found that work with weight training apparatus will improve chronically weak muscle groups and result in better and more injury free performance. In the same tone, entire families have turned to weight training to enhance health and fitness. With weights, all of the muscles in the body can be systematically strengthened. Combine this with a cardio-respiratory activity like running, cycling or swimming, and you have the best all-round fitness program that can be designed. And weight training itself offers its own competitive outlet in the form of bodybuilding and weightlifting.

How Does It Work?

We'll concentrate here on why athletes train with weights to help improve performance in their favorite sport, as this example will serve to illustrate other uses of weight training. Of the various qualities that make up a great athlete — speed, strength, psychological preparedness, endurance, coordination, skill, flexibility, fast reactions and many more — strength can be most easily and quickly developed. Indeed, athletes new to weight training usually notice an immediate upward spurt in their performance. Strength is actually increased by only a single fairly light workout with weights. This strength increase will continue rapidly over a period of many weeks before it gradually begins to slow down. Strength gains of 50 to 100 percent are not uncommon in as short a period as six weeks. But how does this happen?

In simplest terms, muscles grow stronger because a heavier than normal demand is placed on them. The same thing will happen in practicing any sport, but the process can be greatly accelerated by using much heavier resistance than is possible in everyday athletic workouts. Specific strength training will consistently give an athlete a winning edge over a weaker opponent, as all other factors being equal, a stronger athlete will defeat a weaker competitor.

Heavy resistance during an exercise session stresses the skeletal muscles. In adapting to this stress, the exercised muscle grows a bit stronger to accommodate the heavier workload to which it has been subjected. As long as that load intensity remains constant, the muscle strength level will not go up any further. But if a second weight workout can be taken with a slightly greater load put on the muscle, that muscle will again increase in strength. With progressively greater resistance a cycle is established: following each new resistance jump, the muscle tries to stay one step ahead of that load by becoming stronger, while with each new strength gain the athlete can increase the stress put on a muscle to bring about new strength gains. Over a period of this progressive increase of resistance, the net result will be dramatically augmented levels of strength.

Much as in athletic weight training, fitness enthusiasts can increase body strength and avoid such nagging problems as lower backache. And by increasing the poundages lifted, competitive bodybuilders and weightlifters can gain massive development or herculean strength.

But . . .

Despite the effectiveness of weight training for athletic and general physical improvement and despite the already large and still growing number of its proponents, many athletes and fitness enthusiasts still shy away from it. They have heard it will make them muscle bound, slow, tight, too heavy, or that the muscle will turn to fat when they stop weight training. Even their coaches tell them that it will ruin their knees, disrupt their motor patterns and maybe even give them prematurely grey hair. And females endure the most pressure, both socioculturally and physically. "Debbie, it's just not ladylike to lift those big ugly weights. You're going to get huge gross muscles from it. Ugh!"

In actuality, research has shown that the majority of these accusations are completely unfounded. Every locker room and cocktail party has at least one individual with a pet story about how weights made his Uncle George muscle-bound. Numerous scientific research projects, however, have been conducted to refute the idea that progressive resistance training causes such muscular inflexibility.

The first such study was published as long ago as 1950 by Edward K. Capen of Iowa State University (see *Research Quarterly*, Volume 21, Number 1, Pages 83-93). Capen used a control group that trained with ordinary athletic activities and an experimental group that worked for several weeks on a basic schedule of 14 weight training exercises. Tests at the end of the experimental period showed the following results:

1. The experimental group was vastly stronger than the control group.
2. Muscle tightness was absent in the experimental group.
3. In speed events, the experimental group was significantly superior to the control group.

These findings have been verified many times over in succeeding years. Zorbas and Karpovich (*Research Quarterly*, Volume 22, Number 2, Pages 145-148) used 600 subjects to test speed of movement in weight-trained individuals. They concluded that weightlifters had faster muscle contractions than untrained individuals. Masley, Hairabedian and Donaldson (*Research Quarterly*, Volume 24, Number 3, Pages 308-315) tested 69 subjects and concluded that progressive resistance exercise increased athletic speed, coordination and strength while not having a deleterious effect on the subjects. Massey and Chaudet (*Research Quarterly*, Volume 27, Number 1, Pages 41-51) studied the effects of weight lifting on flexibility and found that such training did not result in an overall reduction in range of movement of the body joints.

The above studies were all done in the 1950's, but many recent research projects have yielded the same results. The studies mentioned above, however, should give an indication of both the type of research done and how long the findings have been out.

A second major myth that should be challenged is that muscle gained through weight training will turn to fat as soon as that mode of exercise is terminated. To begin with, it is physiologically impossible to turn muscle into fat except

There are no realistic age limits for weight training. Danny Waller is eight, and men and women in their 80s also enjoy this form of exercise. Children and senior citizens, however, do not use weights as heavy as individuals in their 20s.

through the most circuitous route. And yet you can see many fat former weightlifters. What's the answer?

Well, what really happens is that when weight training is suspended, that athlete or fitness enthusiast tends to revert back to whatever bodytype he/she had before commencing training. Strength gradually wanes, muscle slowly disappears, *and* if fat had been worn away, it will return. As a general rule the return trip to one's starting point will take about the same length of time that it took to build up a muscular body. In the end, individuals who were initially fat will be fat again, the same as their slender counterparts will again be slender.

I might inject one word of caution, however. Those who work out hard tend to burn up large amounts of calories when training. Therefore, it would be wise to cut back food intake as you reduce your training. If this is not done, the excess calories that are consumed but not burned up will be stored somewhere in the body. With a sensible diet, however, no one should have any fear of growing fat from ceasing weight training or, indeed, any sport or physical activity.

The problems that women weight trainees tend to suffer are far more real and result from the social stigma placed on the activity. The tremendous recent boom in female athletics has fostered an interest among women in the value of sensibly undertaken weight training. But many do not have access to good instruction or to other than predominantly male weight rooms at high schools, colleges or YM-YWCA's. Their friends tell them how ugly big muscles are, and if they do go into the weight room the men consider them such a novelty that stares are prevalent, indeed, rampant. It is little wonder that only a handful of women train with weights.

Actually, there is nothing in current research to indicate that weight training is an inappropriate activity for women in a physiological sense. And as far as the sociological pressure is concerned, women interested in weight training should realize that there is safety in numbers. Just take along a female friend or 10 and notice how quickly acceptance follows.

Physically, women will not be able to attain male strength levels, but considerable gains can be made. And while friends might predict the dire consequences of "muscles," recent research contradicts this presumption. Physiologist Jack Wilmore, while at the University of California, Davis, conducted experiments with both athletes and ordinary coeds for several years. He concluded that weight training will not result in women displaying any significant additional muscle tissue.

Visions of hulking male bodybuilders should certainly not discourage any female or male athlete/fitness buff contemplating the use of progressive resistance exercise. Only one man in 100,000 even has the physical potential to reach such muscular development and in many cases he does so by using very extreme methods. He will train three to four hours daily, seven days a week, often taking two or three one-hour-plus workouts each day. He'll gobble hundreds of pounds of food supplements yearly, take male hormone shots and gulp anabolic steroids like candy to build up his huge muscle size. Then to get rid of body fat he will consume only meat and water for a two-month period, as well as resort to the use of thyroid extract to burn off extra fat. Certainly no ordinary athlete or fitness enthusiast — male or female — can afford this time and resource expenditure and will thus not gain appreciable muscle size.

Some Disadvantages

While I am totally convinced of the vast potential benefits of weight work for everyone, I would be the first to admit that some disadvantages to the activity do exist. The first of these is that weight training will build little in the way of cardio-respiratory fitness. A fitness type of program using weights will be presented in a following chapter, but in actuality a long run, bike ride or swim at a moderate pace will produce greater cardio-respiratory fitness.

A second disadvantage to the activity is boredom. The repetitious nature of weight training can almost put some people to sleep in the middle of a workout. This boredom can be countered in many cases by goal-setting, by keeping a written record of progress, or by telling yourself how this or that particular set will help you perform that one iota better in your favorite sport, or how it will improve overall strength and body contour.

The final disadvantage is the slight to moderate weight gain which inevitably results from resistance training for strength. Of course, many readers will be seeking such a weight gain. For those who aren't, it should at least be comforting to know that, unlike fatty tissue additions, any weight gain from progressive resistance workouts will more than support itself, and should result in better results even in bodyweight economy activities.

Advantages

The primary advantage of using weight training lies in its selectivity factor. Specific exercises can be chosen to isolate on and strengthen particular muscles. We'll take a couple of athletic anecdotes to illustrate this point. Weak hamstring muscles, for example, may be adversely affecting sprint speed in a long jumper. Such weak musculature can be very quickly strengthened by doing several sets three times weekly of the leg curl movement. The number of different muscle groups that can be selectively developed in this manner is equal to the number of major muscle groups in the body.

The selectivity factor also becomes quite valuable in rehabilitating injured muscles. Let's take the example of a slightly torn upper chest muscle sustained in an ice hockey game in which the athlete was checked forceably into the boards. The trainer probably immediately iced the muscle to prevent swelling and then began using heat after a two- or three-day rest. With light stretching and gradually greater range of movement, the adhesions are broken down and the athlete returns to action. But gone is the 100-mile-per-hour slap shot and, horrors, the Stanley Cup Finals are only two weeks away! The problem can be solved by quickly rebuilding strength in the recently injured upper pectoral. So selective is weight training that this area can be isolated by doing lateral raises on a 45-degree incline bench. Or if the injury had been to the lower pectoral, the muscles could have been strengthened by doing lateral raises with the head down on a 30-degree decline bench. At any rate, 10 to 12 days and, *voila*, the 100-mile-per-hour slap shot is back!

A third advantage of weight training is the range of resistance possible in each exercise. Unlike gymnastics and calisthenics, which require a certain degree of strength even for elementary moves, weight training resistance can be adjusted downward until as little as 1¼ pounds can be used in each hand. And unlike gymnastics and calisthenic exercise in which

Bodybuilding is one of the two competitive divisions of weight training. Dale Adrian, the 1975 AAU Mr. America, is typical of champion bodybuilders. He stands 5'8'' in height and weighs 200 pounds. His upper arm measures more than 19 inches.

strength cannot progress past the ability to handle bodyweight, weight training can be adjusted upward to almost unbelievable levels. As a good example, world amateur shot put record-holder, Al Feuerbach, does squats with a barbell in the neighborhood of 600 pounds to increase his leg drive, while the female American record-holder in the shot, Maren Seidler, handles approximately 400 pounds in the same movement.

A final advantage, that of quick strength development, has already been mentioned. I had a friend once, a high jumper who had been stuck at 6'2" for over a year. We were in the service together and had plenty of time for workouts, so I was finally able to talk him into adding a short weight session three times a week in the evening. During the first workout, Clint was able to do 10 squats (deep knee bends) with 75 pounds, or about half his bodyweight. He added five pounds to this each session and within four months he was able to do the same 10 repetitions with well over 300 pounds. He gained three pounds of bodyweight, but nearly eight vertical inches on his jump! The latter was a greater improvement than he'd been able to achieve in the two previous years of field workouts alone. Unfortunately, Clint was shipped to Europe a few weeks later and died in a car crash near Munich, the city which had been his ultimate Olympic goal.

Who Are Our Weight-Trained Athletes?

When considering today's well-known champions of sport, an easier question to answer would be: who are our non-weight-trained athletes? Al Feuerbach has been mentioned. He uses heavy weightlifting movements so assiduously that in 1974 he was able to win national titles in both the shot put and in Olympic-style weightlifting, competing in the latter sport against athletes who specialize in this activity. Discus thrower John Powell, javelin thrower Fred Luke, and hammer thrower George Frenn all lift heavy (Frenn has squatted with 840 pounds!). Certainly no track and field weight man can reach national or international caliber today without serious weight workouts. Football teams from junior high school through

Most athletes now train with weights to improve performance in other sports. World record-holder Al Feuerbach has won national titles in both weightlifting and the shot put.

professional levels are deeply involved with weight training as a means of increasing strength, power and muscular body mass. Many pro teams, including the 1975 and 1976 Super Bowl champion Pittsburgh Steelers, have hired strength coaches specifically to supervise weight workouts for their highly paid players.

Athletes in events requiring less brute strength have also turned to progressive resistance exercise in droves. Bill Toomey, the 1968 Olympic Decathlon champion, trained so diligently

Discus world record-holder John Powell is another of the long list of track and field athletes who train with weights. Here he performs the power snatch movement, a key exercise in his discus training program.

with weights for his peak performance that he was able to bench press in excess of 350 pounds, a weight that many competitive powerlifters cannot elevate.

Baseball player Joe Rudi, a member of three Oakland A's World Championship teams, has often been singled out as a professional athlete who has made the very most of his God-given talents. Rudi makes no secret of his use of weight training as a supplement to baseball workouts. Neither does Joe Morgan, superstar second baseman with the '75 World Champion Cincinnati Reds, who exercises several times weekly during the off-season on the Universal Gym that he keeps in his garage.

Among swimmers, exercises in which the athlete pulls on rubber strands have become popular for strength development. Mark Spitz of seven-gold-medals fame used this method as a supplement to his swimming workouts. The University of California water polo team won national titles in 1973 and 1974. The coach of the team, Pete Cutino, calls his athletes "100 percent weight-trained. They wouldn't be on top if they weren't." Cutino also points to the recent flood of great women swimmers from East Germany. "They get to the top faster because they aren't afraid to lift weights."

Basketball players, runners, gymnasts, karate experts, even weekend softball players — the list of weight-trained athletes goes on. The all-female Atoms Track Club of New York holds many American running records and the women in the club are weight-trained. In recent years, crew (rowing) has become such an intensely competitive sport among women that as much as 20 percent of all training during the season is devoted to progressive resistance exercise.

To this point, I have mentioned only American athletes and teams. The list of weight-trained champion athletes could number in the hundreds if one looked at every sport in this country. When one adds to these hundreds the thousands of other champions from around the world, it is easy to see that weight training has caught on strongly among athletes. And little wonder. It gives one the winning edge.

Who Else Trains With Weights?

My own weight training experience lies primarily in the competitive fields of bodybuilding and weightlifting. Counting Olympic-style and power lifters, there are in excess of 30,000 active competitors and another 75,000 to 100,000 trying to muscle their way to the top in the United States. American competitive bodybuilders also number over 30,000 with maybe five or 10 times that number striving to reach a competitive standard. God only knows the numbers who train in these sports outside the United States.

Among those who train with weights simply for the sake of fitness, I know a university president, a few score professors/ attorneys/physicians, even a family with eight children ranging in age down to five (parents and children all work out regularly). I know both men and women who use progressive resistance workouts to improve themselves physically. And I even know two octogenarians who are still plugging away at light barbell and dumbell workouts. So why not hop on the fitness wagon and learn what your body's all about?

2

Off On
The Right Foot

Tragically, a huge amount of misleading or downright false training information lurks in most weight rooms. There always seems to be someone who is willing to distribute his "wisdom" free of charge, but a beginner, or even more advanced trainee, should weigh each new piece of advice carefully before following it. The purpose of this chapter is to give you the straight dope about weight training. In my 15 years of involvement with the activity, I've seen people make all the mistakes you can imagine. Each of these could have been avoided with proper instruction. This book is your tool for doing it right, so read on.

Where To Train

There are basically five types of facilities available for weight training. The first of these and the least recommended is the commercial health spa. Such facilities are well-equipped, but are also very expensive to attend and often high-pressure sales techniques are used to snatch your hard-earned dollars. And since these establishments cater to a money-bags businessman/ businesswoman clientele, managers tend to discourage anyone who wants to really train hard in the belief that such "weirdo types" will frighten away paying customers.

Training at home is another approach. It has both advantages and disadvantages. While it allows for workouts at any time during the day or night and costs nothing after an initial equipment investment, it does present a danger to new and inexperienced trainees of forming bad exercise habits. It must be noted, though, that this problem can be minimized if a weight training friend can be persuaded to sit in for the first two or three workouts to offer advice and guidance. He/she can also answer questions as they come up in later weeks. It has been my experience that many individuals and families start out at an organized public weight room, gather all the necessary information, and then end up working out in their basement or garage free from the distractions always present at big public gyms.

For home gym trainees, equipment is relatively easy to obtain. A small barbell set of about 100 pounds will do nicely for a start. Any of the weight training magazines available at major newsstands will advertize barbell-dumbbell sets, but freight must be paid on these and ordering one by this means will often entail a wait. Large department and sporting goods stores also sell sets and are probably your best bet if you want to buy a new equipment package.

Personally, I would recommend buying a used set through the want ads. I recently was able to buy over 500 pounds of weights at 10 cents a pound for a women's rowing club simply by advertising in one of the weekly "nickel want ad" tabloids. Thousands of people buy a set, go great guns for two months and then lose interest, so that the weights end up collecting dust in the attic. Many are anxious to get rid of the weights and willingly sell at quite a loss. (Incidentally, breaking in slowly and gradually — covered in this chapter — will help promote training longevity.)

When selecting a set of weights, bear in mind that vinyl-covered weights will not scratch floors, but that the cast iron version is far more durable. The vinyl plates are filled with sand or concrete and often split open under heavy use. And don't be put off by rusty metal plates. A couple of dollars' worth of

Modern health spas have sprung up like mushrooms after a rain. They are usually well-equipped for all but the most advanced individual, but high-pressure sales tactics and high expense are principal drawbacks to training in this type of gym.

spray paint will make them as good as new, and you usually won't even need to wield a wire brush.

YM-YWCA's and commercial gyms (they are both equipped like health spas, but don't have all the chrome) are next in order of preference. They charge reasonable yearly dues, but are usually quite well-equipped. In addition, commercial gyms offer quality instruction to new members. The primary disadvantages include a periodic cost and the requirement in many cases to fit one's exercise schedule to the hours that the "Y" or gym is open.

High school or college weight rooms are the best bet in the event that a new trainee is a student. The quality and selection of equipment will vary, but the equipment will always be adequate for novices. Instruction in weight training is offered at both high school and college levels and is generally of high quality. At colleges, ask around to see who teaches the best activity classes and arrange to take his/her section.

Sources Of Instruction And Information

Basic training advice is available from several sources. Obviously, I have to defend this book as one of the better sources of instruction. It contains clear illustrations and descriptions of each exercise, sound training advice, as well as enough workout programs to suit just about any purpose. But there is always the possibility of error in interpreting instructions in any book, no matter how clear the author might think the book is. That is the manifest weakness of this publication and others like it. I hope that you can use this book as a source of advice and information, and maybe supplement it with hints from more experienced friends or school instructors. The combination will give you the best possible quality of instruction.

Gym instructors are good sources of information, but they are inclined to lose interest in individuals rather quickly. But at big gyms you will find what I consider to be a very good source of advice. That's the man or woman who has trained with weights for some time. In many cases the man will appear as hulking as a big bear, but when asked he is invariably a font of readily given and authoritive information. The woman with weight training experience can usually be recognized by the confident and speedy way she moves from exercise to exercise and not by her appearance. Many of these men and women have trained for years with weights and have read widely on the subject. If anyone knows how to build strength, they do. All you need to do to get information from them is ask.

On the other side of the coin, the worst sources of information are the many weight-training magazines. Occasionally they will publish a profile on some famous athlete or champion team. This will include a description of how that person or team trains, but for the most part articles in these magazines are aimed at advanced male athletes in training to improve musculature or competitive weightlifting strength, and not athletic ability or fitness. Seldom do these periodicals publish fitness material for the average person or athlete, although bodybuilders and lifters consider these periodicals as valuable as the Bible.

Training Frequency

Strength and muscle mass increase while resting, so it is necessary to allow at least one full day off between training days. With this in mind, the best schedule for beginners and intermediates consists of three non-consecutive training days each week. Commonly, training sessions are scheduled on Monday, Wednesday and Friday, but any other three-day-per-week scheme is acceptable. Novices are cautioned, however, that they should never train two days in a row. Such a practice might bring good short-term results, but over the long haul will do the body little good when compared to a standard three-times-weekly schedule.

Advanced weight trainees can, if they like, work out more often than thrice weekly by following a split routine. This will be discussed in detail in the chapter on advanced training techniques, but a split routine consists of exercising half of the body one day and the other half the next. This still works each bodypart only three times weekly, but it allows for shorter and more intense training sessions.

When To Train

Long observation has shown that setting a regular time for workouts each exercise day is a far better practice than training at odd or irregular hours of the day. If a demand is consistently put on the organism at, say, 3:00 p.m., the body will soon adjust its natural energy cycles for optimal performance at 3:00 p.m. This results in a more energetic and productive training period with the weights.

In warmer climates, it is often a good change of pace to weight train outdoors. This kills two birds with one stone—you get exercise and a good tan.

Intense weight workouts should always be done either after one's regular sports or fitness workout, or if a great deal of training time is available at least two hours before. The biggest reason for this is the so-called "muscle pump." When a muscle is worked hard with weights or in any other demanding movement, blood rushes into the tissue after such exertion to supply oxygen and help flush away fatigue wastes. This blood flow during exercise is much greater than usual and results in a temporary tightness in the muscle, as well as a temporary increase in muscle girth. This "pump" condition causes a coarsening of motor control, as well as a slowing of muscular movement. The "pump" is, of course, temporary and will last only until the muscle has been able to flush away the toxins and renew its food and oxygen supply. This process seldom takes more than two hours.

The second reason for doing weight workouts after your regular sports training or aerobic session is almost too obvious to be mentioned. Essentially, you are training for a specific sport, be it track, football, rowing, field hockey, etc. This takes up many hours of work on conditioning and technique. Why use up energy on massive weight workouts that could be better utilized in your regular workout? In other words, weight training is a supplement and should be treated as such.

Weight workouts should also be scheduled at least one hour before or after eating. Training too soon after a meal will lead to sluggish exercise sessions due to the large amount of blood required in your stomach to digest food. Eating right after training is equally unwise because heavy exercise tends to have a depressant effect on the appetite for about an hour after training.

Equipment Orientation

A barbell is the basic unit for progressive resistance exercise. Usually it is supplemented by dumbbells, which are merely shorter handled barbells. A typical adjustable barbell and dumbbell set is illustrated in the appendix.

Barbell bars come in various lengths and are made of

several types of material. The weight of each bar unloaded
depends on the above two factors plus the size of collars and
their composition. Each adjustable bar should be weighed and
that weight noted for use as a base poundage. You can then add
plates to the bar to arrive at the required resistance for each
exercise.

Many adjustable bars have a hollow metal tube called a
sleeve fitted over the bar. This sleeve helps the bar to revolve
when hand positions are changed. The bar itself and its attached
plates are heavy and reluctant to spin freely in the air, while a
sleeve will revolve about the bar and save sore hands and wrists.
The sleeve is commonly machined with cross-hatched grooves
called a *knurling* so your grip will be more secure. In the event
that a sleeve is not part of the barbell or dumbbell, the bar itself
is almost always knurled.

Inside collars serve two functions. By tightening a heavy
bolt threaded through the collar and against the bar, a collar can
be set securely in place. Thus set, it keeps the sleeve centered on
the bar and prevents the barbell plates from shifting position
inwardly along the bar.

Barbell plates are typically heavy iron or semi-steel discs
with a hole punched through the center so the plates can be
fitted on the bar. Most plates are flat, but many sets currently
on the market have tapered edges and interlocking features that
result in quieter performance. A substantial number of barbell
sets being sold have vinyl covered concrete or sand plates which
won't scratch floors. As mentioned early in this chapter, these
plates are not as durable as metal plates. In addition, most
serious weight trainees frown on vinyl plates because they are
quite bulky and it is difficult to fit enough of them on a bar to
make up a substantial poundage. The most common barbell
plate sizes are 1¼, 2½, 5, 7½, 10, 12½, 15, 20, 25, 50 and 100
pounds.

Once the desired number of plates has been fitted on the
bar, they are secured with an outside collar. Training without
this outside collar on the bar is inviting a minor disaster, as
unsecured plates tend to slide off the end of a bar.

In most large commercial gyms, YM-YWCA's, health clubs, universities and schools, one will encounter fixed barbells and dumbbells. In this case a rack of barbells is available in graduated poundages from about 15 pounds to over 100, usually in 10-pound increments. Dumbbells usually range from 10 to 110 or 120-pound pairs in five-pound increments. Each barbell and dumbbell will have the correct poundage permanently inscribed on the bar, thus eliminating the need to concern oneself with adding up the weights on the bar. The main advantage of fixed weights, however, is that you don't have to bother changing plates on and off an adjustable set. Instead of wasting time changing the weights, you need only select the correct barbell from a nearby rack.

As far as adjustable sets are concerned, dumbbells differ from barbells in that they usually have no inside collars. This presents a problem in that plates on only one side at a time can be changed. If both outside collars are loosened at once, the revolving sleeve invariably ends off center.

In well-equipped weight rooms you will also see Universal Gyms, lat pulleys, floor pulleys, squat racks, bench press racks, parallel bars, leg curl-leg extension machines, wrist rollers, situp boards, incline benches, decline benches, and perhaps even Nautilus machines of various types. The exact function of each piece of equipment will become evident in the next chapter as we explore various exercises for each part of the body.

Some Basic Exercise Terminology

In every weight training schedule, one is required to do several different exercises. Many different sets of varying numbers of repetitions are done in each exercise. The word "exercise" has many different dictionary meanings, but in the sense that we're using it here, it is the particular movement that is performed. A pushup is an exercise, as is its barbell equivalent, the bench press. When one does a series of pushups or bench presses, each individual effort is called a repetition (or rep for brevity). The entire series — whether it is eight, 10 or 100 reps — is called a set. After doing one set, a trainee can rest a couple of minutes and perform a second set, and even a third, fourth and fifth if the program calls for that number.

Before The Workout

There are two essential steps to be taken prior to training. The first of these is to dress properly for exercising. In warm weather, little more than shorts and a T-shirt are necessary. In cooler weather a full sweat suit will keep the body warm and help to prevent injuries. In choosing a training outfit, pay special attention to selecting shirts and pants that are either made of stretchy material or are sufficiently loose fitting to allow total freedom of movement. Bras for women or athletic supporters for men are optional.

Although many individuals prefer to train barefooted or in sandals, sturdy shoes with an arch support are recommended. Bare feet are fine until the day you accidentally drop a heavy barbell plate on your toes! Besides, advanced trainees often use very heavy poundages while standing, thus arch supports are necessary to insure good foot health.

A second pre-workout necessity is to warm up thoroughly. If you started your car on a cold wintery day and tried to drive right off, the engine would cough, sputter and probably die. But if you let the engine idle for a few minutes, the car will be warmed up and run efficiently. The human body is very similar to an automobile in that it, too, requires a warmup period before it is able to work efficiently. A proper warmup speeds up the pulse rate, makes muscle and connective tissues more pliable and resistant to injury, and actually allows one to lift heavier weights than would be possible without a warmup.

Any five- or 10-minute bending and stretching session will provide a sufficient warmup, but try the following series of movements:

1. Jog in place for 100-200 steps.
2. Rotate trunk.
3. Do 20-30 jumping jacks.
4. Bend and stretch back muscles.
5. Perform 10-20 squatting movements without weights.

6. Do 15-20 pushups or modified pushups.

7. Follow with 15-20 situps.

8. Conclude with another 100-200 jogging steps.

Ideally a warmup should leave one feeling fresh and ready to tackle the weight training workout. One should feel warm and supple. You might even be perspiring slightly. Devise any sort of five- or 10-minute warmup system you desire, but never rush into weight training without such a warmup. Training without warming up is only inviting injury and less than maximum results.

Correct Form

It is absolutely essential in every exercise to move the weight along the full range of motion, from complete extension of a joint to complete contraction of a muscle on every repetition. This will develop the greatest strength in all muscle groups, which is especially valuable for many athletes. Failure to move the weight along the full range of motion will result in incomplete strength development. And there is no excuse for partially developing any muscle's strength potential if an Olympic medal might be waiting in your future.

Training Speed

The length of rest between each set depends to a great degree on how "heavy" you are training. With light weights rests of only 20-30 seconds are possible, while longer pauses are necessary when lifting very heavy weights for power. Rest pauses of more than two minutes are discouraged, however, because long rests will allow the body to cool, whereupon injury becomes more likely.

A second speed factor is the tempo of the movement itself. The first repetitions should be done slowly and with great control. After that the tempo should be gradually accelerated until the final three or four repetitions are done as fast as possible. Going slowly at the beginning is necessary because research has shown that most weight training muscle and joint injuries occur during the first two or three repetitions. Working these reps under full control virtually eliminates the chance of injury.

Schedule Changes

Due to the repetitious nature of weight training, boredom can occur after several weeks on the same schedule. To combat this, it is advisable to change the program each four to six weeks. Often one only needs to change the order of exercises, but usually it is necessary to substitute new exercises for each muscle group.

In addition to changing schedules, it is also necessary to take occasional layoffs from training. About one week off after three months of steady workouts is normal. This allows the body to recycle and reconsolidate, which results in even better workouts when training is resumed.

Breathing

How to breathe while exercising with weights is a common concern even among advanced trainees. There are basically three schools of thought on the subject. The first is that one should breathe on the exertion phase of each movement, while the second advocates breathing on the recovery phase. I subscribe to a third theory, namely that it doesn't matter when you breathe. As long as you are taking in the amount of air required, you're doing fine.

Multiple Sets

In the weight training classes I teach, one question always seems to come up: "When you say I should do three sets of an exercise, should I go ahead and perform all of the sets before moving on to the next exercise, or should I go all the way through the program doing one set of each movement and then come back to pick up the extra sets with other trips through the recommended schedule?"

Well, the answer boils down to whether you're after great strength or strength tempered with some endurance. Those who are interested in pure strength should do all of the recommended sets of an exercise before moving on to the next. This is especially important when many sets of an exercise are done,

Captain Al Jones of the Marine Corps is one of the world's fittest men. He's done 27,003 consecutive situps, swum 100 miles non-stop, and broken more than 15 world records. Weights are an important part of his conditioning program.

each set with heavier weights than the last. This type of schedule will be recommended in many pure strength sports in the chapter on exercise programs.

For more concentration on endurance, go through one set of each exercise and then pick up the additional sets on subsequent circuits through the program. A unique form of weight training using this circuit process to develop fitness is explained in greater detail in the advanced training techniques chapter.

Safety

When using very heavy weights, several precautions must be taken. I mentioned the use of collars early in the chapter. Their use cannot be over-emphasized. Always use collars, especially with common barbell sets, but also with the heavier Olympic-type barbells. A large number of athletes do squats, bench presses and deadlifts without using collars on their Olympic sets. But I have seen back injuries occur when all of the plates slid off one side during 400- to 500-pound squats.

The use of a weightlifting belt is also important when doing movements like squats, deadlifts or power cleans with heavy poundages. This belt comes in a four-inch width for standard competitive weightlifting and in a much wider training model which gives proportionately greater abdominal and lower back support. Of course, the wide belt is preferable.

A final safety factor is to use spotters when doing heavy bench presses and squats. There have been at least two cases of male bodybuilders choking to death in recent years while bench pressing alone and not being able to complete a heavy repetition. In order to keep the bar from crashing down on *your* throat, always have a training partner stand at your head end of the bench to make a rescue attempt if the bar won't go up. Squatting can be spotted by a single partner standing right behind you, but a better method is to use two helpers, one on each end of the bar.

Progression

Progression is the very foundation of weight training for

strength and increased muscle mass. To get these gains, the resistance on each exercise must be progressively increased. There are three ways to do this. The easiest is to add plates to the bar, or you can increase the number of repetitions, *or* you can keep the poundage and reps the same while decreasing the length of rests between sets. In actuality, a combination of increasing both the number of repetitions and the weight on the bar is most often used.

Here is an example of proper progression for the curl exercise:

Day 1	Day 5
55X8	60X10
Day 2	**Day 6**
55X10	60X11
Day 3	**Day 7**
55X12	60X12
Day 4	**Day 8**
60X8	65X8, etc.

One should be able to add a new repetition (or more than one) to each exercise with little difficulty. Note that each time you are able to reach the top guide number for repetitions (12 in the above example), you should add weight and drop the reps back down to the bottom guide number.

Men can usually increase the resistance for upper body exercises by five or 10 pounds each time they up the weight, while for the legs and back, a jump of 10 to 15 pounds should not be excessive. Women can halve the male jump figures to arrive at correct increases.

As long as you keep progressively increasing resistance, your strength and muscle mass should also increase. This is, of course, assuming that your diet is good, you get sufficient sleep, and you do not rest too long between sets.

Sleep And Rest

If you're an active athlete, you should already be well aware of the importance of sleep and rest. The body rebuilds itself from any type of workout while sleeping or relaxing. Your energy reserves are like a bank account. If they are used up faster than replaced, you're eventually going to go broke. You'll simply have to keep putting enough back into the bank to keep the account up. About eight hours of sleep is standard for most people, but nine or 10 hours a day isn't uncommon when in hard training. I know one top-ranked former national champion weightlifter who averages 12 hours of sleep a day!

Rest is also important throughout the day when working out hard, whether it be weight training, running or boomerang throwing. Since the old energy bank has only so many coins in it, why waste them on late nights and high living?

Diet

Health/fitness devotees and athletes as a group are far more conscious of diet nowadays than average people. They know what to eat and what kind of junk foods to avoid. There's an old saying that "you are what you eat." A wholesome and balanced diet will build a strong and healthy athlete, while a cola-and-hamburger regimen will yield, shall we say, less than ideal results.

My own view is that an athlete's diet should be heavy on proteins from meat, fish, fowl, eggs and milk products. At the same time, fat intake should come from nuts and unrefined vegetable oils for unsaturated fats. Carbohydrates for energy should come from natural sources like fruit and vegetables, whole grains and honey. Steer clear of refined products of any sort, particularly sugar. For supplements you might try vitamin C, wheat germ oil and dessicated liver tablets (listed in order of importance). Fitness enthusiasts should have about the same diet, but more fresh fruits and vegetables should be included.

Break-In And Muscle Soreness

Muscle soreness is a common condition when one is starting training or resuming workouts after a long layoff. It is primarily due to decreased body efficiency in eliminating fatigue toxins from the muscles. Thus, such toxins as lactic acid are not flushed from the muscles and these toxins cause the pain. Secondary sources of muscle soreness include outright

Ann Turner finds weight workouts to be a valuable adjunct to her flatwater kayak training. Only 19, Ann was ranked first in the Western Hemisphere in 1975 in all three women's kayak events.

muscle strain, but this is usually restricted to very advanced trainees who are capable of exercise with weights close to their actual physical limits.

Fortunately, muscle soreness disappears rather quickly. With several workouts, the body is able to become more efficient in eliminating toxins and the soreness will be gone. At this point, only workouts that are considerably harder than usual will cause a recurrence of the problem.

There are ways to prevent soreness resulting from those first few workouts. Basically, it all spells "break in slowly." For the first few sessions, use weights that are very easy to handle. At my peak, I have bench pressed more than 400 pounds, but after a layoff recently due to school pressures, a mere 185 pounds proved to be enough for me to reach for the analgesic balm. Breaking in slowly also means doing only one set of each recommended exercise the first day. From that point you can slowly add exercises as the body grows accustomed to heavier and greater loads.

If soreness does occur, there are one or two things you can try. Massage is one, but sometimes it can be relatively painful. It will, however, get you back in training faster. Heat is a better choice. It's hard to beat a hot bath or whirlpool for near instant relief. And a final method is to do the same workout for the next two days with no rest day between. This hurts as much as massage, but I have noticed that it eliminates even severe soreness very quickly.

Let's Go

Well, these are the basics necessary to get started safely and sanely in weight training. The next chapter will list and describe exercises for each muscle group. This will give you a pool of exercises from which you can construct workout programs, whether you're training for a specific sport or are simply interested in self-improvement.

3

The Exercises

Here we will present several exercises for each muscle group in your body. As you can see, each exercise is illustrated by photos and a written description. If you have never worked out with weights, carefully observe the photos while reading the text. Pay special attention to body positions. In Chapters Four, Five and Six, you will be able to put these exercises to good use, as they will be inserted into suggested programs for a variety of sports and physical activities.

Leg Exercises

In most sports, the legs are of prime importance. In the case of many older athletes, leg weakness or injury often spells the end to a long career. Usually this condition could have been forestalled by proper weight training. Leg strength and health, of course, are important to anyone, and an individual is usually only as young as his/her legs. The legs can be divided into four separate areas — the *quadriceps* on the front of the thigh, the *biceps femoris* or hamstrings on the back of the thigh, the hip musculature and the calves.

SQUAT

Left: Important points to remember in the starting position for the squat are foot stance and a straight back. Note the use of a sturdy rack to support the barbell between exercises. Right: In the bottom position of the squat, the head should be up and the back must be held as upright as possible.

The *Squat* or deep kneebend is the best all-round lower body exercise. Hold a weighted barbell behind your head and across your shoulders. Pad the bar for greater comfort when using heavy weights. Start with feet about shoulder width and toes turned slightly out. Tighten your back and leg muscles and squat down as low as possible. Return to starting position and repeat.

It is important to keep your head up and torso as upright as possible throughout the entire movement. A good way to do this is pick a spot on the wall above eye level and keep the eyes focussed on it while squatting. Some will say that squats ruin knees, but the only way for this to happen is to collapse and bounce at the bottom of the movement.

FRONT SQUAT

Left: Front squats are very similar to regular back squats. Note closely how the barbell is held across the deltoids, with the hands acting mainly as balance points. This allows a person to use very heavy weights in the front squat. Right: Again, the torso is held upright.

 Front Squats are an exact duplicate of the previous exercise, except that the barbell is held in front of the neck instead of behind. For maximum comfort, rest the bar across your deltoids with the elbows held high. This variation of the squat exercises the thigh muscles just above the knee more completely than any other. With all squat exercises, you can experiment also with narrow or wide foot stances.

BENCH SQUAT

Although squatting does not injure the knees, many individuals are still afraid of going into the low position. In this case, it is often wise to use a bench to stop the downward motion. Be sure not to rest in the sitting position.

    Bench Squats can be done with the bar either in front or in back of the neck. Straddle a bench and squat down until the buttocks lightly touch the bench. Recover and repeat, but be very careful not to bounce at the bottom. Just touch lightly and be sure not to actually sit on the bench. Enormous weights can be used, so be very sure to have spotters. The easiest way to ruin a $150 chrome-vanadium bar is to drop it onto a narrow bench while the bar is loaded to 600 or 700 pounds.

PARTIAL SQUAT

Partial squats to varying depths are great strength builders. Left: A quarter squat, in which more than 1000 pounds can be used by trained men. Note the use of knee wraps. Right: The half-squat position. Notice the use of a lifting belt for lower back and abdominal support.

Partial Squats can also be done with the bar either in front or back. They involve simply going a fraction of the way down and then recovering. Quarter, half and three-quarter squats are commonly done. This is a tremendous exercise for thigh strength, as weights up to half a ton can be used by men, and 500-600 pounds by trained women.

JUMPING SQUAT

The use of jumping squats will help to build better spring into the thighs and calves. The athlete accelerates from the full-squat position and jumps into the air at the completion of the movement. Relatively light weights are used for jumping squats.

Jumping Squats are usually done with the bar behind the neck. The special feature of this movement is that it should be accelerated so rapidly at the finish that the athlete literally jumps into the air as high as possible. Consistent use of this movement builds athletic strength in the thighs and also gives calf muscles a stiff workout. You might prefer doing jump squats with a dumbbell in each hand instead of holding a barbell behind the neck.

STEP-UP

Many vertical and horizontal jumpers prefer the use of step-ups to increase leg spring. The higher the bench, the more difficult this exercise becomes.

The *Step-Up* is a common exercise and is used sans weights in the famous Harvard Step Test of cardio-respiratory fitness. Place a barbell behind your head and step up onto a bench with the left foot. Step back down and then up with the right foot. Alternate until each leg has done the required number of repetitions. Step-ups can also be done with a pair of dumbbells in place of the barbell.

LUNGE

*Left: Dumbbells can be used effectively in the lunge exercise.
Right: Note in the barbell variation that the knee is ahead of
the foot and the back leg has the toe turned slightly out.*

The *Lunge* movement is an excellent thigh and hip
exercise. Place a barbell behind your neck and start with the
feet parallel and about shoulder width apart. Step forward with
the left foot as far as possible. Lower the body until your right
knee touches the floor, recover to starting position and follow
the same process for the right leg. In the low position, the front
knee should be well ahead of your foot.

UNIVERSAL GYM LEG PRESS

The leg press station on a Universal Gym offers a very convenient way to exercise the thigh muscles with heavy weights. Note how the handles at the sides of the seat are used to maintain correct upper body position throughout the movement.

The Universal Gym offers a *Leg Press* station in which the frontal thigh muscles can be conveniently exercised. Simply sit in the seat, grab the handles to steady your position, and put your feet on the pedals. Then straighten the legs, return to starting position, and repeat. I have found that the lower set of pedals gives a much more direct thigh movement. For maximum range of motion, it is essential to have the seat moved as far forward as possible.

VERTICAL LEG PRESS

Several points should be noted in these photos. Notice the hands on the rotating stopping mechanisms, which are rotated outward during the movement. Once a set is completed, these stops are rotated inward to support the weight. The hips are directly under the platform, which usually weighs about 50 pounds when unloaded.

Some gyms have a *Leg Press* machine that moves on vertical runners. The person using the machine reclines on his/her back while exercising the leg muscles. All of these machines come with a wedge-shaped board on which to recline. Place your hips at the low end of the board and position yourself so the hips are directly below the foot platform. Such machines also have stopping mechanisms that can be rotated out of the way to allow for greater range of motion. To perform the movement, place feet on the platform and alternately straighten and bend the legs.

LEG EXTENSION

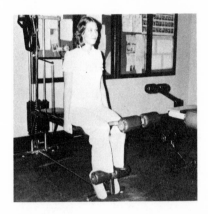

An important point to remember when doing leg extensions is to pause momentarily at the top position of the movement. For variety, or when one knee is injured, try exercising one leg at a time.

Most weight rooms have a *Leg Extension* machine for exercising the frontal thighs. Simply sit on the end of the table, hook your in-steps under the bottom set of rollers and straighten your legs under resistance. Return and repeat. Many physical therapists recommend an isometric contraction of 10 to 15 seconds at the top of this movement to strengthen quadriceps muscles when the knees are injured.

LEG CURL

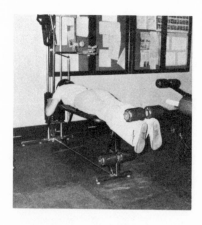 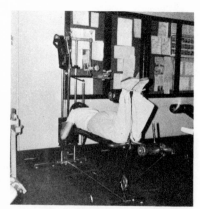

A leg curl is the only movement that directly exercises the hamstring muscles at the back of the thighs. With heavy weights, it is important to hold on to the bench to maintain upper body position.

The *Leg Curl* can be done on the same apparatus as leg extensions and is a superior movement for directly working the hamstrings at the back of your upper legs. Lie face down with your heels hooked under the upper pair of rollers. Bend the legs as much as possible. Then return them to the starting position and repeat. Try to keep the upper body down on the table and get the maximum possible range of motion. Universal Gyms often have a leg curl and leg extension station.

TOE PRESS

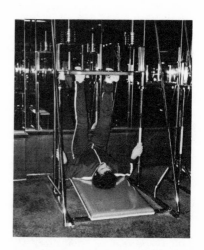

Toe presses can be done on either the Universal Gym leg press station or the vertical leg press apparatus. Do the exercise slowly and with a complete range of motion.

The *Toe Press* movement can be done on the Universal Gym leg press station to develop the calf muscles. Sit in the leg press seat and press the pedals until your legs are locked out straight. Slide your feet off the pedals until only about one third of each foot (i.e., the balls of the feet) remain on the pedals. Extend the toes out as far as possible, then pull them back toward the body as much as you can, and repeat. Try to achieve maximum range of motion, particularly in stretching the calf muscles. This movement can also be done on the vertical leg press apparatus.

DONKEY CALF RAISE

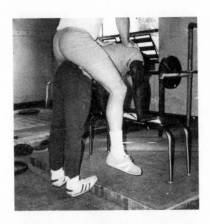 

The donkey calf raise may be a bit humorous to watch, but it is one of the most effective movements for building calf strength and contour. The partner should sit as far back on the hips as possible. Note how the edge of a platform is used to allow for stretching the heel below the toes.

To do a *Donkey Calf Raise* you will need a heavy training partner and a 4" x 4" block about 18 inches long. Stand on the block with only the balls of the feet in contact with the block. Lock the legs, bend at the waist and rest your hands on a bench for support. With your heavy partner astride your hips for resistance, lower your heels until they're well below the toes. Then rise up on your toes as high as possible. This is one of the very best calf exercises.

SEATED CALF EXERCISE

A barbell can be rested across the knees while seated to effectively exercise the calves. With heavy weights the bar can be padded with a towel. Note the use of a high block, as well as the hand postition to balance the bar across the knees.

The *Seated Calf Exercise* requires a bench, the 4" x 4" block and a barbell. Sit on the bench with toes on the block and barbell resting across your knees. You might need to pad the bar for comfort. From this position, raise the heels up and down. This movement is especially good for developing the *soleus* muscles which lie under the *gastrocnemius* of the calf.

STRADDLE HOP

The straddle hop exercise helps to build athletic spring into the calf and thigh muscles. Note the hand position used to steady the bar across the shoulders.

The *Straddle Hop* is simply a barbell version of the jumping jacks familiar to any junior high school boy in a physical education class, and to many of the girls as well. Rest the bar across your shoulders and hop up and down, alternately placing the feet apart and together. You can use dumbbells held in both hands at your sides for variety.

ONE-DUMBBELL CALF EXERCISE

The calves can be trained rather easily by holding a single dumb-bell in one hand. The free hand is used for balance only.

The *One-Dumbbell Calf Exercise* requires a dumbbell and our old friend, the 4" x 4" block. Stand on the block with your right foot, the heel off the block, and hold the dumbbell in your right hand. Wrap your left leg around the right leg and balance yourself lightly with your left hand. Rise up and down on the toes and be sure to alternate legs with each set.

CALF MACHINE

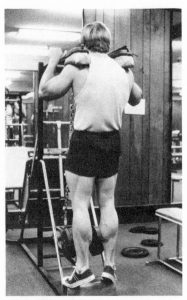 

The calf machine makes lower leg exercise very convenient. Both legs can be worked at once, or one at a time. Toe positions should be changed occasionally to work the calves from more angles. You can point toes in, out or straight ahead.

Many gyms have a *Calf Machine* on which one can do calf raises. It looks like a yoke with a weight attached. Stand with your heels off the block and the yoke across your shoulders. From this position you can easily do the up-and-down heel movement for building calf strength and size.

BARBELL CALF RAISE

By resting a barbell across the shoulders, one can stress the calf muscles by rising up and down on the toes. If you do not have a block of wood to exercise on, you can put your toes on a pair of thick barbell plates.

The *Barbell Calf Raise* can be done standing on the block with a heavy barbell across your shoulders. Rise up and down on your toes. This is a good exercise if you are able to master the inherent balance problem.

Back Exercises

There are very few physical activities which do not require strong back development in one way or another. Some activities such as rowing or heavy manual labor require special strength, while figure skating or Sunday golf do not require as much development. All individuals, however, will need a strong lower back in order to avoid injuries to that area. Of course, lower back problems can severely limit your activities in sport or life in general.

For our purposes here, we will divide the back into three areas. The upper back, which includes primarily the *trapezius* muscles (known colloquially as the "traps"), requires several exercises. The middle back includes primarily the *latissimus dorsi* (or "lats"), while the lumbar group of the lower back consists of the *erector spinae*.

The *Clean* is half of a competitive lift called the clean and jerk. Stand with feet about shoulder width apart and grasp the bar at about shoulder width, palms towards your body. Dip your hips, flatten your back and keep your head up (this is the basic pulling position for lifting all heavy weights from the floor). Start the bar from the floor with leg strength and then follow through with back and then arm pull. When the bar reaches its maximum height, jump under it in a deep squat, catching the bar at your chest. Stand up with the bar to complete the lift.

The clean is a great overall back exercise, but is very difficult to learn properly. You may need to seek coaching from an experienced competitive weightlifter to master the lift. The clean is also occasionally done in split style, but this method is not recommended, as it makes the knee of the back leg vulnerable to injury.

CLEAN

This sequence of the clean movement reveals several key points of that competitive lift. Note the low hip position at the start, the straight arms during the pulling phase, the total body extension and the arm follow-through, and finally the high elbow position as the bar is caught at the chest. The clean will be complete as soon as the lifter stands up with the barbell.

SNATCH

Two positions are shown for the snatch. It starts in the same manner as the clean, except that the arms are spread wider. The middle portion of the pull is the same, still with arms straight. The barbell is caught at arms' length in the deep-squat position and the lift is completed by standing up.

The *Snatch* is another competitive lift that's difficult to learn. Start with the same position as for the clean, but with the hands spread much wider. Pull as high as possible and jump under the bar in a full squat, catching the bar this time with arms locked straight. Stand up to complete the lift. Only about 65-70 percent of the poundage lifted in the clean can be used in the snatch. You may also need coaching for this movement.

POWER CLEAN

Here are the middle pull and the finish position for the power clean. Note how the bar is fixed at the chest by slightly dipping the legs. The depth of this squat is, of course, much less than for the full clean. This is the first half of the clean and press exercise

The *Power Clean* is similar to the clean, but the bar is racked — or caught at the chest — without squatting under it. A weight approximately equivalent to your best snatch poundage can be used in power cleaning. This lift works the thighs and whole back, but particularly the trapezius. Most people find that a slight knee dip at the top of the movement is helpful to catch the weight at the shoulders.

POWER SNATCH

These two photos illustrate the top pull and finish position for the power snatch. Again notice the body extension and arm fol-follow-through at the top of the pull. A good strong pull will send the bar about two feet higher under its own momentum than shown here. The movement between these two positions is lightning fast.

The *Power Snatch* is also similar to the snatch, but the bar is fixed overhead with no squat. Again a lighter weight must be used, one in the range of 70-75 percent of your best snatch. The power snatch is used by many as a warmup for a regular workout. It is a fine upper back developer. Again, a slight dip will help you fix the weight at its top position.

UPRIGHT ROWING

The key to obtaining the most benefit from the upright rowing motion is to lower the barbell as slowly as you raised it. Recent research has shown that lowering a heavy weight and resisting it on the way down is a superior way to develop strength.

The *Upright Row* is a very fine trapezius movement. Stand with feet a comfortable width apart. Take a narrow grip (about six inches wide) in the center of the bar, with palms towards your body and the weight across your thighs. Pull the barbell upward close to the body until it reaches chin level. Emphasize a high elbow position at the top of the lift and then resist the weight on the way down. The upright row is also a fine shoulder muscle developer and can be done using the floor pulley station on a Universal Gym machine.

SHOULDER SHRUG

Barbells or dumbbells can be used to do the shoulder shrug exercise for upper back development. Note in the left photo how high the shoulders can be shrugged at the top position. Always be sure to use maximum range of motion in all exercises.

The *Shoulder Shrug* is the single most direct exercise for trapezius strength development. Stand erect with a shoulder width overgrip (palms towards the body) and bar across your thighs. In shrugging, the arms are non-functional, serving only as a means by which the barbell is suspended from your shoulders. Sag your shoulders forward and down as much as possible and move to a finish position by shrugging the shoulders as high as possible. This movement can also be done in rotating fashion with two dumbbells or by grasping the handles on a Universal Gym bench press station.

CHINNING

The ordinary *Chin* is one of the best movements for strengthening the *latissimus dorsi* muscles of the middle back. This muscle group pulls the upper arms down and back, and chinning the bar involves this same down-and-back motion of the upper arms. You can chin in front or behind the neck, with wide, medium or narrow grips, or with either under- or overgrips. All of these variations in different schemes can be combined in various ways to prevent boredom. Most women feel they don't have enough strength to do chin-ups, but I once trained a female rower who was finally able to do 15 correct chins.

LAT MACHINE PULLDOWNS

You can either kneel on the floor, as in these two photos, or sit while doing the lat machine pulldown. Note that the arms are straight at the start of the pull, and the bar touches the base of the neck at the bottom of each repetition.

A *Lat Machine Pulldown* motion is exactly equivalent to the chin, and is a good substitute if one does not have the strength to do chins. Either kneel or sit under the machine and vary grips along the same range as for the chinning motion. Universal Gyms have a station for lat pulldowns.

LAT MACHINE PULLDOWNS

Four variations of the lat pulldown. Upper left shows the medium overgrip and upper right the narrow overgrip. The two bottom photos show the medium reverse grip, but with different bars. The lower left bar is cambered, while the one at lower right is straight.

BENT-ARM PULLOVER

The upper two photos illustrate the start and finish positions for a bent-arm pullover. A barbell, single dumbbell or two dumbbells can be used for this movement.

The *Bent-Arm Pullover* is a fine movement for both middle back and chest muscle strength. Lie back on a high flat bench. Take a narrow overgrip, with the bar resting on your chest. Maintaining this bent arms position, lower the bar in a semicircle back over your head and ultimately as close to the floor as possible. Then, keeping your elbows as close together as possible, pull the bar back over to the starting position. You can also do this exercise with two dumbbells or one dumbbell held in both hands.

STRAIGHT-ARM PULLOVER

 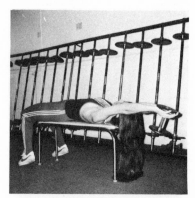

Here again the upper two photos show the range of motion for the straight-arm pullover. A single dumbbell can be held in both hands, or you can use two dumbbells or a barbell.

The *Straight-Arm Pullover* is an excellent exercise for both middle back development and rib cage expansion. Reclining on a high bench, take a shoulder width grip (or narrower one, if you prefer). Lock the arms and start with the barbell directly over the chest. Lower the barbell in a semicircle back over the head to a position as close to the floor as possible. Return to starting position and repeat. For variety, try using a pair of dumbbells or a single dumbbell held in one hand.

BENT-OVER ROWING

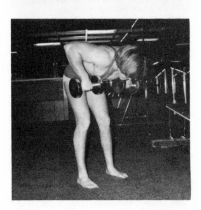

Bent-Over Rowing is a very versatile exercise that can be done with a barbell, two dumbbells, or one dumbbell at a time, alternating hands. With a barbell, use one of three grips: wide, medium or narrow. Bend over with torso parallel to the floor and legs slightly bent. The bar will be a little off the floor. Pull it from the hanging position until it touches the mid-chest area and repeat. The movement is exactly the same with two dumbbells. However, two dumbbells give you the option of rowing alternately. When using a single dumbbell you can rest your free hand on a bench for better support. Rowing is great for the lats and also works the biceps.

SEATED PULLEY ROWING

If you happen to have droopy shoulders, the seated rowing movement will help correct the condition. Notice the use of either a straight bar or two pulley handles.

The *Seated Pulley Rowing* movement requires a low pulley with a bar handle. Most Universal Gyms have this station and some public gyms have such a pulley installation. Sit facing the pulley with your torso upright and your hands in an overgrip on the bar. Pull the bar to your lower chest as if you were rowing a boat and repeat for the required number of reps. This works virtually the same muscles as bent-over rowing.

DEADLIFT

At the start of a deadlift, the hips are dipped a little lower than in the upper left photo. The finish position is reached when the torso is upright and the shoulders pulled back. A special lifting belt is usually used.

The *Deadlift* is one of the finest full body power exercises and is also a great lower back developer. Assume the basic pulling position with a shoulder width overgrip and pull the bar up until your body is stiffly erect. Return the bar to the floor and repeat. With heavy weights you will want to use a mixed grip, one hand in an overgrip and the other in an undergrip. This will effectively prevent the bar from rolling out of your fingers. Trained male lifters can do almost 900 pounds in this exercise.

STIFF-LEG DEADLIFT

Stiff-leg deadlifts are usually done while standing on a low bench. This allows the barbell to be lowered a bit more, resulting in a greater stretch in the hamstrings and lower back.

The *Stiff-Leg Deadlift* exercises the lumbar muscles of the lower back and also has a beneficial effect on the thigh biceps. Start with the barbell in the regular deadlift finish position and legs locked out straight. Bend at the waist until the barbell touches the floor, then return to starting position. To make the exercise more advanced, stand on a low flat bench and touch the handle to the bench at the lowest point of the movement. This results in a much longer range of motion.

BACK HYPEREXTENSION

Even with a sore back, most individuals can do back hyperextensions to strengthen the lumbar musculature. If a bench like the one in these photos is not available, have a training partner hold down your feet. A weight can be held across your neck for added resistence.

The *Back Hyperextension* is a lower back exercise that can be done even when the lumbar area is sore. Some Universal Gyms have a station for this, but I personally prefer a high table. You will need a partner to hold your legs down. Lie face down on the table and slide off until only your legs are still in contact with the table. Have your partner sit on your legs. Begin with your upper body hanging straight down, then raise it as high as possible. Lower your upper body back down and repeat. When the movement becomes easy, you can hold a barbell plate behind your head for added resistance.

GOOD MORNING

By bending over while holding a barbell across your shoulders, you can effectively exercise the lower back and hamstrings. This movement has an effect on the body very similar to that of the stiff-leg deadlift.

Good Morning exercises are a convenient way to exercise the lower back and thigh biceps with a light barbell. Start with the bar across your shoulders and feet a comfortable distance apart. From an erect position and with legs locked out, bend over as far as possible and recover to starting position. Some athletes also perform this movement with legs unlocked and using much heavier weights. This method helps to build greater low back strength.

Chest Exercises

The pectoral muscles of the chest function to move the upper arms forward. The pectorals consist of two muscles groups, the *pectoralis minor* (the smaller upper pectoral) and the *pectoralis major* (the large lower pectoral). By varying the angle of the bench used for chest exercises, an athlete can selectively develop strength in the upper chest, the lower chest, or work the entire pectoral in one fell swoop.

The *Bench Press* is one of those movements that works the entire pectoral area. In fact, most athletes consider bench presses — or benches, as they're called — to be the best upper body exercise of all. To perform it, lie back on a bench and start with the barbell at straight arms length directly above the chest. An overgrip with hands spaced slightly wider than shoulder width is most often used, but a very wide collar-to-collar grip or a narrow grip with hands touching can be used to give different effects. In fact, any grip along the entire bar is appropriate. At any rate, lower the barbell straight down until it touches the mid-chest and press back to arms length. The Universal Gym also has a station for doing bench presses.

BENCH PRESS

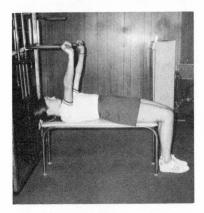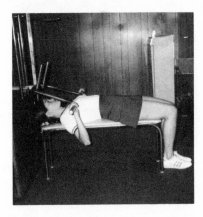

Bench presses can be done either with a tree bar or on the bench press station of a Universal Gym. Note in the upper two photos how two supports are attached to the bench. This makes it much easier to move a very heavy weight into position for bench presses.

INCLINE BARBELL PRESS

If you lie back on a 45-degree incline bench and do presses, you will be putting most of the emphasis on the upper pectoral muscles. Some incline benches have a support rack similar to that attached to flat benches.

The *Incline Barbell Press*, which is a variation of the bench press, places stress on the upper pectorals. The same grips and manner of performance holds for inclines as for benches. Additional stress can be placed on the upper pectorals by forcing the elbows back, striving for a right angle between the upper arm and torso. When you first try inclines, the bar will probably want to go in every direction but up. Don't worry about it, as motor difficulties can be ironed out with only one or two sessions. Just use a light weight to learn the movement.

DECLINE BARBELL PRESS

You can isolate the stress in the bench press to affect the lower pectoral muscles merely by lying back on a decline bench. As with flat and incline benches, these decline benches occasionally have a rack attached to assist one with heavy poundages.

The *Decline Barbell Press* with head at the lower end of a slanted bench is also a variation of the bench press. This exercise places more stress on the lower pectorals. Most athletes find that this movement is most easily performed on an inclined situp board with the angle set at about 30 degrees.

DUMBBELL BENCH PRESS

Dumbbell Bench Presses can be done as alternatives to the three different angles of barbell bench press. At first it might prove difficult to control dumbbells, but using a dumbbell in each hand will allow for greater range of motion. When using a barbell, the bar will contact the chest and cut short the movement. But with dumbbells, the hands can go much lower than with a barbell, resulting in better strength development.

STRAIGHT-ARM LATERALS

Straight-Arm Laterals are a very direct type of pectoral exercise isolating out triceps involvement. Choose either a flat, declined or inclined bench, depending on which section of the pectoral you wish to develop. Start by holding two light dumbbells at arms' length over your chest — the dumbbells touching each other. Keeping your arms straight, lower the dumbbells out to the side, allowing them to descend as close to the floor as possible. Return to starting position and repeat.

BENT-ARM LATERALS

Lateral raises with bent arms can be done on incline, decline and flat benches. The key to the movement is to bend the elbows slightly at the bottom position.

Bent-Arm Laterals are a variation of straight-arm laterals, and allow for more comfort in some cases. Many individuals feel some strain on the inside of the elbows when doing the straight-arm variation. This small pain can be easily eliminated by slightly bending the elbows throughout the movement. You will also find that more weight can be used with bent arms than with the arms straight.

PARALLEL BAR DIPS

Parallel bar dips are a key upper body exercise, and are especially good for stressing the lower pectoral. Notice the extremely low position attained at the bottom of the movement.

   Parallel Bar Dips are excellent for lower pectoral strength development, as well as a fine movement for deltoid and triceps strength. In my opinion, dips are equal to bench presses for overall upper body development. Support the body at arms' length over the parallel bars. Lower the body as much as possible, preferably until the shoulders touch your hands. Press back up to arms' length and repeat. By leaning forward, a bit more stress is placed on the lower pectorals, while an upright posture of the body places more stress on the triceps.

Deltoid Exercises

The deltoid muscles of the shoulders are extremely important in almost all physical activities. These muscles function to move the upper arms over a very wide range of motion. Deltoids move the arms backwards, forward, to the sides and to hundreds of angles in between.

Three sections of the deltoids (called *heads* of the muscle) help account for its wide variety of movements. The *anterior head* (frontal section) helps to move the arms toward the front, the *medial head* (side section) primarily moves the arms to the sides, and the *posterior head* (rear section) moves the arms to the rear.

To develop the three deltoid heads, one uses basically lateral raise movements and pressing exercises. As a general rule, pressing will result in greater deltoid strength and development when done in lower reps of six to eight, while laterals are best done in the 12- to 15-rep range.

It might also be noted that many chest exercises tend to strongly affect the deltoids. These include barbell and dumbbell bench presses, incline presses and decline presses, as well as parallel bar dips.

The *Military Press* is the most basic of all shoulder exercises. Take a shoulder width overgrip on a barbell and bring the barbell up to your shoulders. Stand stiffly erect with feet about 20-24 inches apart. Press the barbell from the shoulders to extended arms' length overhead. Return to shoulder level and repeat. Be sure the bar comes close to your face on both the upward and downward path.

Militaries, as they're called, are a fine exercise for triceps, trapezius and upper chest, as well as deltoids. The movement can also be done seated for variety and to make the exercise more strict (i.e., with less involvement from other muscle groups). The Universal Gym has a station for military presses.

MILITARY PRESS

With either a free bar or using the Universal Gym, military presses are the basic shoulder exercise. Notice the complete range of motion. This is the second half of the clean and press.

DUMBBELL PRESS

Dumbbell presses can be done using both arms, or one at a time. When exercising a single arm, the free hand is usually used to steady the upper body.

The *Dumbbell Press* is a fine variation of the military press. Simply press the dumbbells from the shoulders to the overhead position. The dumbbells can be pressed either together or alternately, lowering one at the same time the other goes up. Hands can be held so the palms face forward or face each other, and the exercise can be done seated or standing. Many individuals prefer to do dumbbell presses holding a single dumbbell in one hand and then alternating arms for the required number of sets. With one arm presses, grasp an upright pole with your free hand for better balance and then lean toward the exercising arm for greater range of motion.

PRESS BEHIND NECK

Presses from behind the neck strongly influence the anterior head of the deltoid muscle, as well as the upper back and triceps. This is a very popular movement with bodybuilders, as it very quickly adds width to the shoulders.

The *Press Behind Neck* is a third variation of the basic pressing motion. The only differences are that a slightly wider than shoulder width grip (three inches wider on each side) is used and the bar is pressed each time from a point on the trapezius muscles of the upper back. Many athletes will do this exercise seated. One interesting variation is to alternate presses from the front with those from behind the neck. These and all other pressing exercises strongly effect the anterior deltoid, but also have an influence on the medial and posterior sections.

FRONT LATERAL RAISE

The *Front Lateral Raise* strongly exercises the anterior head of the deltoid. The basic movement is done standing with a shoulder width overgrip on a light barbell. Start with the arms stiff and the barbell held across the upper thighs. Keeping the arms straight, move the barbell in a semicircle from thighs to arms' length overhead. Return and repeat. You can also use two dumbbells, raising each one alternately, or raising both together. A fourth variation is to hold a single dumbbell in both hands. If you use this variation, you might like to pad the dumbbell with a towel.

SIDE LATERAL RAISE

The lateral raise isolates the action on the deltoid muscle by eliminating the triceps involvement of pressing exercises. Palms down stresses the medial deltoid head, palms up the anterior head.

The *Side Lateral Raise* works the anterior and medial deltoid heads. Hold a light dumbbell in each hand with arms straight and at your sides. Move the dumbbells — or bells, as they're colloquially called — from this starting position in a semicircle out to the sides until they meet directly overhead. Return and repeat for the required number of repetitions. Keep the palms down throughout the movement. By turning the palms up, stress is shifted almost entirely to the frontal deltoid and much more weight can be used than with palms down.

BENT-OVER LATERALS

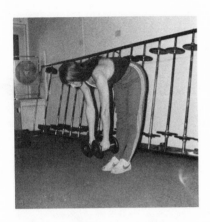 

Bent-over laterals isolate the action primarily on the posterior head of the deltoid, with a bit of assistance from upper back muscles. The torso should be kept in the same position throughout the movement.

Bent-Over Laterals, a variation of the lateral raise, stress the posterior heads of the deltoids. Bend over at the waist until the torso is parallel to the floor. Bend your legs slightly and suspend the dumbbells directly below your chest with arms straight. From this starting position, raise the dumbbells straight out to the sides until they are above your torso. Lower and repeat.

PRONE INCLINE LATERALS

By lying face down on an incline board and doing lateral raises, you can isolate the muscle involvement to posterior and medial deltoid heads. If you are trying to build shoulder width, this is a key movement.

Prone Incline Laterals are a very effective movement for developing side and rear deltoid strength. Lie face down on a 45-degree incline bench with two dumbbells hanging down in your hands. Raise the bells out to your sides until they are higher than your torso, lower and repeat the movement. Be sure to keep the arms straight and raise the bells a bit out in front of the head throughout the exercise.

PRONE LATERALS

Prone laterals are exactly equivalent to bent-over laterals. They are a bit more comfortable to do, however, if you happen to have a sore back, because they remove strain from the lumbar vertebrae.

Prone Laterals primarily work the posterior deltoids. The exercise is very similar to the Prone Incline Laterals, except that you lie face down on a high flat bench, rather than an inclined bench. Raise the dumbbells directly out to the sides as high as possible. Lower the bells slowly in this and all lateral raise exercises, as research has shown that considerable strength can be developed by resisting as a weight is lowered.

Upper Arm Exercises

The upper arm musculature is comprised of biceps and triceps muscles. The biceps are flexors which bend the arm, while the triceps are extensors which straighten the arm. A number of exercises that directly affect the biceps and triceps will be presented in the following pages, but the arm muscles are heavily involved in many other upper body exercises already presented. Triceps come into play in all pressing exercises, including bench presses, incline presses, decline presses, military presses, presses behind the neck, and all dumbbell variations of these exercises. Biceps are strongly influenced by upright rows, bent rows, lat pulldowns and chins of all types.

BARBELL CURLS

Barbell curls can be done with a regular shoulder width grip, or with hands narrower or wider. Curl the bar up to the chin.

Barbell Curls are the basic biceps exercise. Take a shoulder width undergrip and stand erect with the barbell across your upper thighs. Pin your elbows against your sides and move the bar with biceps strength from thighs to chin. Be sure to keep the elbows in tight and do not swing the bar to get it started. For variety, try a very wide grip or a narrow grip about six inches wide. To make curls even more stressful on the biceps, do them with your back pressed against a wall.

DUMBBELL CURLS

If barbell curls are painful to your wrists or elbows, try doing them with dumbells. This variation allows for a more natural movement of these two joints and often prevents such soreness.

Dumbbell Curls have many variations, all of which have great potential for developing biceps strength. Bells can be curled together or alternately, palms forward or facing each other, while you're standing or seated. Many athletes lack sufficient wrist and elbow flexibility to comfortably do barbell curls, in which case dumbbell curls are a fine alternative.

PULLEY CURLS

Pulley curls can be done either while standing or lying down. Either variation is quite effective. Some pulley machines even allow you to do alternate curls by gripping individual handles.

   Pulley Curls can be done on the floor pulley station of the Universal Gym. Simply grasp the pulley handle while standing upright with the handle across your thighs. Curl from this position or assume the same position lying on your back on the floor. Either way, pulley curls will stimulate the biceps thoroughly.

INCLINE/SUPINE CURLS

Incline and supine curls are a more advanced form of dumbbell curls. In either position, the body is braced and will not move to assist the curl, thus making the movement a more direct biceps exercise.

Incline Curls are an effective method of almost totally isolating the biceps muscles. Lie back on a 30- or 45-degree incline bench with the dumbbells hanging straight down. Curl the bells to your shoulders either together or alternately. An even more severe type of biceps exercise is the *Supine Curl*. Lie back on a high bench with the bells hanging down and curl from that position. Be careful in the second movement to break in very slowly, as it is an extremely difficult biceps exercise and can result in very sore muscles.

CONCENTRATION CURLS

The concentration curl is a favorite movement with most body-builders because it helps to build better-shaped biceps. Note the use of magnesium chalk on the palms to keep sweaty hands from slipping on the bar.

The *Dumbbell Concentration Curl* helps build maximum contractile power in the biceps. Sit on the end of a bench with a single dumbbell held in your exercise hand. Brace your exercise elbow against your knee so that your upper arm does not move during the exercise. From this braced starting position, curl the dumbbell up to your shoulder, lower and repeat. Try to twist the little finger as far toward the body at the finish as possible.

BARBELL FRENCH PRESS

The *Barbell French Press* in its many variations is the basic triceps strength builder. We will focus on the standing variation for the sake of description. Take a six-inch-wide overgrip on a barbell. Stand with the bar at extended arms' length directly overhead. Keep the upper arms and elbows totally stationary. Lower the barbell along a semicircular arc to the back of your neck by moving only the forearms. Reverse the procedure to return to starting position. You should feel stress in your triceps. Variations of this movement include performing it seated, or lying on a flat, inclined or declined bench.

DUMBBELL FRENCH PRESS

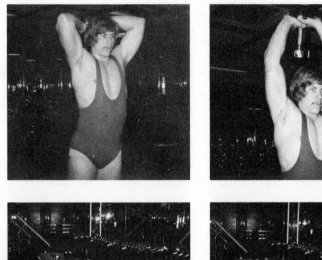

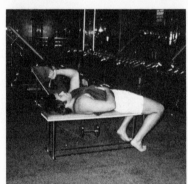

A large number of variations can be thought up for dumbell French presses. Here are three.

The *Dumbbell French Press* also has many variations and is a fine triceps exercise. All of the barbell variations can be done with a single dumbbell held in one hand, a single dumbbell held in both hands, or a dumbbell in each hand. In essence, enough possible variations exist to permit a different Dumbbell French Press exercise each day for a period of a month or more. Be very careful to keep the upper arms stationary in all French Press variations. Moving the upper arms diminishes the value of the exercise for triceps improvement.

LAT MACHINE PRESSDOWN

The key to this exercise is to keep the elbows pinned in to the sides. Move the bar of the lat machine from your chin to the tops of your thighs.

The *Lat Machine Pressdown* movement can be done on a Universal Gym or separate lat machine. Take a narrow overgrip on the lat bar (anything between hands touching and hands six inches apart). Start with your arms straight, bar across your thighs and elbows in tight at your sides. Keeping the elbows in, move the bar in a semicircular motion from thighs to chin by moving only the forearms. Press back to starting position and repeat for the required number of repetitions.

DUMBBELL KICKBACK

A dumbbell kickback can be done using either one hand at a time or both hands together. When using one hand, the free hand can be braced on a stool or bench to help steady the upper body.

The *Dumbbell Kickback* develops maximum contractile power in the triceps. Bend over at the waist and rest the non-exercising hand on a low bench for support. Hold a light dumbbell in the other hand with the exercise arm held at a right angle. From this starting position, straighten the arm out behind you. In the finish position, your arm will be straight and parallel to the floor. The dumbbell kickback can also be done with two dumbbells at once.

Forearm Exercises

The muscles of your lower arms serve a myriad of functions and are used in virtually all physical activities. They come in handy in all gripping movements and motions in which the hands are flexed or extended. Forearms provide the final impetus in nearly all throwing events, especially baseball/ softball pitching and shot putting.

REVERSE CURL

Reverse curl variations include the regular shoulder width grip, and a narrower grip with hands about six inches apart. Because of the angle of the wrist joint, wide reverse curls are seldom done.

The *Reverse Curl* is done with a barbell and affects the powerful muscles on the outer and upper part of the forearm. Take a shoulder width overgrip on a barbell and stand erect with the barbell against your thighs. Pin your elbows to your sides and curl the barbell up to your chin. A good variation of this movement is to take a narrow grip, but about 20 percent less weight can be handled with such a grip.

WRIST CURL

Wrist curls can be done with a barbell, two dumbbells, or a single dumbbell held in alternate hands.

The *Wrist Curl* with a barbell works the powerful muscles on the inside of your forearms. Take an undergrip of about shoulder width. Sit on a low bench with your forearms resting along your thighs. Your fists should not be supported by your knees. Bend the fists as far down as possible, even rolling the bar down your fingers. From this position curl the bar up as high as possible, flexing your wrists as hard as you can. This movement can also be performed holding one dumbbell or two.

REVERSE WRIST CURL

Reverse wrist curls can be done in the same variations as when curling with palms up. Most individuals find that less weight can be used palms down, however.

Reverse Wrist Curls stimulate the smaller muscles on the outside of your forearms. Such curls are done exactly like wrist curls except that a reverse grip is used. Again, dumbbells can be used as a variation. An additional variation is to do the exercise while kneeling beside a low bench, your forearms positioned across the bench.

ZOTTMAN CURL

With Zottman curls, it's dumbbell up, palm up, and dumbbell down, palm down.

The *Zottman Curl* is a combination of regular and reverse curls with dumbbells. It is also an alternate curl. Curl one dumbbell upward with the palm up. At the top, rotate your hand so the palm is turned downward as the dumbbell descends. As the first dumbbell goes down, the other starts up. It may take a few sessions for the movement to become automatic, but as long as you remember "dumbbell up, palm up — dumbbell down, palm down," there's not much chance to go wrong.

WRIST ROLLER

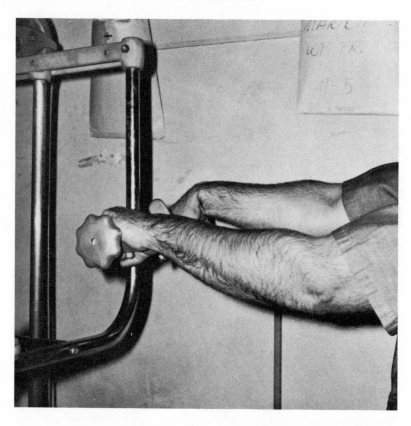

A *Wrist Roller* apparatus is included with many Universal Gym installations and as a separate unit in most big public gyms. Simply grasp the roller and roll it with exaggerated hand actions in a forward direction and then in a reverse direction. The exercise can be done with alternate hands or both hands at once. If a wrist roller apparatus is not available, you can make a suitable substitute with a 1½" x 16" dowel and 10-foot piece of clothesline cord. Drill a hole in the middle of the dowel and thread the cord through it. Attach a weight to the free end of the cord, stand on a high bench and wind the rope up on the dowel both forward and backward.

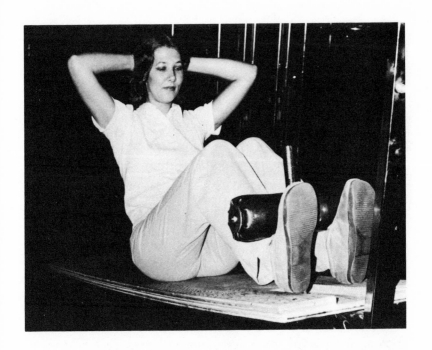

Abdominal Exercises

The muscles of your abdomen function to support the middle of your body and to help draw up your legs. These muscles can also provide protection for vital internal organs.

Generally speaking, abdominal exercises are done with light weights in relatively high repetitions (in the 20 to 100 range). For added power, however, many of the exercises in this section can be done with added weight. The only exercise that I would caution against doing with heavy weights is the side bend. In that movement, heavy weights will very quickly widen the waist, resulting in a certain loss of aesthetic appeal.

SITUP

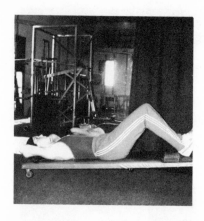

Countless variations exist for the situp movement. The most important point to bear in mind in all variations is to keep the knees slightly unlocked. This keeps strain off the lower back.

The *Situp* in its many variations is the most effective of all abdominal exercises. It is best done with your feet held down by a training mate, a barbell, or the strap or roller of an abdominal board. Never do situps with straight legs as this style puts an unnatural strain on the lower back. Do them instead with legs slightly bent. Also be careful to curl up rather than jerk the torso upward on each repetition.

Situps can be done with your body flat on the floor, legs slightly bent, or — for added difficulty — with your body on an incline, legs elevated. The higher the incline, the more difficult the exercise becomes. Resistance can also be added by holding a barbell plate behind your head. Some athletes prefer to do situps by twisting to alternate sides with each repetition.

SITUP ACROSS A BENCH

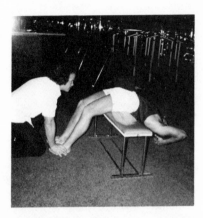

A situp across a bench is an advanced exercise that places great strain on the frontal abdominals. Don't try this one until you can do at least 100 consecutive situps on the floor.

Situps Across a Bench are a very advanced stomach muscle exercise. Sit on a low bench with feet under a barbell or held down by the partner. Bend backward until your head touches the floor and then sit back up. You should experience a terrific stretch in your abdominal muscles when performing this movement.

LEG RAISE

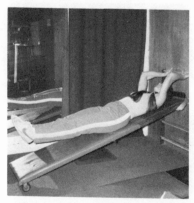 

If you tire of situps, leg raises exist as a good alternative. Try them either flat on the floor, or on an incline. The higher the incline, the more difficult leg raises become.

The *Leg Raise* movement is excellent for frontal abdominal development. Lie down either on a mat or an inclined abdominal board and grab something to hold your upper body steady. With legs slightly bent, raise them up to a position at least vertical to the torso. Some athletes prefer to raise the legs as far as possible, even to the point where their ankles touch their head.

KNEE-UP

 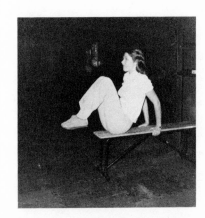

Knee-ups are a rather mild form of frontal abdominal exercise. Keep your upper body braced with your hands while performing the movement, and pull your knees up near your chest.

The *Knee-up* is perhaps the mildest of all frontal abdominal exercises. Sit on the edge of a low bench. Lean back and support your upper body with your hands on the edge of the bench. Extend your legs out straight and then pull your knees up to your chest, completely bending your legs at the same time. Return to starting position and repeat.

FROG KICK

If you have a strong grip, you can try doing frog kicks while hanging. This has the dual benefit of exercising the abdomen and taking kinks out of your lower back.

The *Frog Kick* is an advanced version of the knee-up. Hang from a high horizontal bar with your feet off the floor. From this position pull your knees up to your chest, lower and repeat. Many sore-backed athletes have found that this exercise serves as a free chiropractic session.

HANGING LEG RAISE

A very advanced form of leg raise can be done while hanging from a bar. Try to bring your legs up at least parallel to the floor. Most bodybuilders like to use this movement to build ripples of muscle in the frontal abdominals.

The *Hanging Leg Raise* is the most advanced form of leg raise. Start from the same position as for the frog kick. From there, slowly raise your legs until they are parallel to the floor. Lower and repeat. There is a tendency for the body to swing during this exercise. This can be prevented by having a partner hold your hips in one place.

PARALLEL BAR LEG RAISE

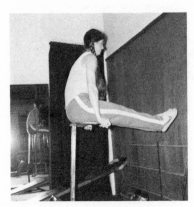

Another advanced leg raise can be done while supporting the body on parallel bars. Try to keep from swinging the body as the legs are raised.

The *Parallel Bar Leg Raise* is another variation that can be done to keep training more interesting. Support your body on a pair of parallel bars. As in the Hanging Leg Raise, slowly raise your legs up until they are parallel to the floor. Gymnasts use a very similar movement as part of their parallel bars routine.

SIDE BEND

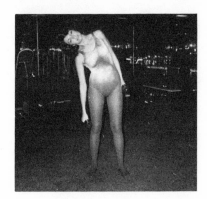 

Here are three possible variations of the side bend. Be sure to use light weights and high repetitions in this movement. Heavy weights will build the muscles of the sides and make the waist look wider.

The *Side Bend* exercises the external oblique muscles at the sides of your waist. Place a light barbell across your shoulders and behind your neck. From a standing position, alternately bend as far as possible to each side. This movement can also be done with two dumbbells, or a single dumbbell used in alternate hands.

TWISTING

Twisting is excellent for both oblique development and for waist and lower back flexibility. Place an unloaded bar behind your neck and wrap your arms around it. Stand upright. From this position, twist the torso as far as possible to each side. Try to keep your hips in the same position throughout the movement. Twisting while seated makes it easier to keep the hips from twisting right along with the upper body. A third variation of the twisting motion is performed bent over and with a wide foot stance. This variation places some stress on the lower back as well as the sides.

Neck Exercises

Strong neck muscles are not only essential for such sports as football and wrestling, but they can also save your life in a car accident or bad fall. I personally credit neck strength and development for the ability to walk away from a fall from my motorcycle while going nearly 100 miles per hour. I hit a seagull while on a beach speed trial, was thrown from the bike, landed on my head, and walked away with only sore muscles and minor scratches. (Take a hint, Evel!)

The musculature of your neck is rather unique in that it will move your head to a myriad of positions. You can incline your head forward, backward, to either side, or to any angle in between. This type of mobility demands a number of different angles of attack when exercising the neck.

WRESTLER'S BRIDGE

The wrestler's bridge is a key movement for all athletes who wrestle. Neil Darrow of the Universtiy of California wrestling team illustrates the regular and front bridges.

The *Wrestler's Bridge* is a very commonly used movement to strengthen the front and back neck muscles, as well as the sides of the neck to some extent. Lie on your back on an exercise mat and bridge up on head and feet. Rock forward and backward, as well as side to side. For added resistance, hold a plate on your chest. A variation of this exercise is to perform it chest down instead of up.

PARTNER HAND PRESSURE

If you can find a partner, try exercising your neck with his or her help. Incidentally, this movement is best done co-ed.

Partner Hand Pressure can be used rather conveniently for building neck strength. Kneel down on hands and knees on a mat. Have your partner stand in front of you. Bend your head back as far as possible and resist as your partner pushes your head forward to a chin-on-chest position. Push your head back to starting position while your partner resists sufficiently to allow only a slow upward movement. For each side of the neck, the same procedure can be used. In this case the partner can best push on the side of your head with one hand while grasping your opposite shoulder with the other. This allows for maximum leverage from your training mate.

SELF HAND PRESSURE

Several variations of neck movements can be preformed by using your own hand pressure.

Self Hand Pressure is probably the most convenient method of neck exercise, as it requires no equipment and no training partner. You can provide your own resistance with your hands and can move the head in any direction desired.

HEAD STRAP

Head straps aren't expensive and they offer a very convenient form of neck exercise.

The *Head Strap* can be used to develop the neck. Attach resistance in the form of a dumbbell or some loose plates on the end of the chain. The basic movement for the back of your neck is to hang the chain down the front of your body and then move the head forward and back. To work the front of your neck, hang the chain down the back. The sides of the neck can be exercised by inclining your body to the side and hanging the chain to the same side.

4
Programs For Sports Improvement

In this chapter we will offer basic break-in schedules applicable to any athlete, male or female, who has not yet had the opportunity to train with weights. Then an in-season and off-season program will be presented for as many sports as possible. Each of these specialized programs is suitable for both men and women. With each schedule, approximate starting poundages will be stated in percentages of your own bodyweight. Such percentages are intended as guidelines only; you may well be forced to adjust the poundages upward or downward. In the following programs, you might come across an exercise that cannot be done with the quipment you have available. In that case, simply look in the exercise pool in Chapter Three, pick some exercise for the particular bodypart and substitute it in the program.

Beginning Programs

Here are three different schedules for the complete novice. One is intended for those individuals who have access to only a barbell-dumbbell set, while the second is for those who only have access to a Universal Gym. The third program, which is the most highly recommended, is for use in a gym with both types of apparatus. All three schedules will develop strength in virtually all muscle groups except the neck. Remember to break in slowly.

Barbell-dumbbell programs

Exercise	Sets	Reps	Men	Women
1. Clean and Press	1	15-20	35%	25%
2. Bench Press	2-3	8-12	45%	35%
3. Military Press	2-3	6-10	40%	30%
4. Bent Rowing	2-3	8-12	45%	35%
5. Upright Rowing	2	8-12	30%	20%
6. Barbell Curl	2	8-12	30%	20%
7. Wrist Curl	2	15-20	30%	20%
8. Squat	3	12-15	40%	30%
9. Stiff-Leg Deadlift	1	12-15	40%	30%
10. Barbell On Knees Calf Work	3	15-25	50%	40%
11. Situps	1	25-100	---	---

Universal Gym Program

Exercise	Sets	Reps	Men	Women
1. Leg Press	3	12-15	80%	70%
2. Bench Press	3	8-12	45%	35%
3. Lat Pulldown	3	8-12	40%	30%
4. Military Press	2	6-10	40%	30%
5. Pulley Curl	2	8-12	30%	20%
6. Lat Pressdown	2	8-12	30%	20%
7. Calf Press	3	15-25	80%	70%
8. Situps	1	25-100·	---	---

Combined Program

Exercise	Sets	Reps	Men	Women
1. Clean and Press	1	15-20	35%	25%
2. Leg Press	3	12-15	80%	70%
3. Bench Press	3	8-12	45%	35%
4. Lat Pulldown	3	8-12	40%	30%
5. Military Press	2	6-10	40%	30%
6. Upright Row	2	8-12	30%	20%
7. Barbell Curl	2	8-12	30%	20%
8. Stiff-Leg Deadlift	1	12-15	40%	30%
9. Calf Press	3	15-25	80%	70%
10. Wrist Curl	2	15-20	30%	20%
11. Situps	1	25-100	---	---

Archery Program

Two keys to good performance in the sport of archery are muscle steadiness and consistency in duplicating each step of the shooting step. Shakiness during the draw or when you reach your anchor point — the point on the side of the head where your pulling hand rests at full draw — is usually due to weak muscles, particularly in the arms, shoulders and upper back. Archers need not train the lower body, but should do the following program two or three times each week both in and out of season. The program should be done after shooting.

Exercise	Sets	Reps	Men	Women
1. Bench Press	2	8-12	45%	35%
2. Bent Rowing	3	8-12	45%	35%
3. Military Press	2	6-10	40%	30%
4. Upright Rowing	2	8-12	30%	20%
5. Standing Laterals	2	12-15	5%	3%
6. Bent Laterals	2	12-15	5%	3%
7. Lat Pressdown	2	8-12	30%	20%
8. Situps	1	25-100	----	---
9. Back Hyperextension	1	8-12	----	---
10. Side Bend	1	15-50	10%	7%

Baseball/Softball Programs

Key muscle groups in baseball and softball include the forearms, deltoids and upper back, but as with most sports virtually all of the body's skeletal muscles come into play. The following out-of-season weight training schedule should prove effective when combined with a good running program:

Exercise	Sets	Reps	Men	Women
1. Clean and Press	1	15-20	35%	25%
2. Leg Press	2-3	15-20	75%	65%
3. Leg Curl	2	12-15	25%	15%
4. Calf Press	3-5	20-30	80%	70%
5. Bench Press	2	12-15	40%	30%
6. Lat Pulldown	3	12-15	40%	30%
7. Upright Row	2	12-15	30%	20%

8.	Press Behind Neck	2	8-12	35%	25%
9.	Barbell Front Raise	2	12-15	20%	10%
10.	Reverse Curl	2	12-15	30%	20%
11.	French Press	2	12-15	30%	20%
12.	Wrist Curl	2	20-30	25%	15%
13.	Reverse Wrist Curl	2	20-30	15%	10%
14.	Situps	1	25-100	---	---

During baseball season, a light and fast maintenance workout should be taken twice a week at roughly evenly spaced intervals (e.g., Monday and Thursday, or Tuesday and Friday). This will keep strength levels at a peak and prevent late season tail-offs in performance. The following program can be performed after a workout or game:

1.	Clean and Press	1	15-20	35%	25%
2.	Squat	1	20-30	40%	30%
3.	Calf Press	1	30-50	70%	60%
4.	Bench Press	1	20-30	35%	25%
5.	Lat Pulldown	1	20-30	35%	25%
6.	Reverse Curl	1	20-30	20%	15%
7.	Wrist Curl	1	30-40	20%	15%
8.	Situps	1	25-100	---	---

Basketball Programs

Basketball requires leg and arm strength with, in some cases, a need for added bodyweight. Actually playing basketball is the best endurance conditioner for basketball, while weights will provide needed strength when done in relatively high reps. For added bodyweight, perform each exercise with heavier weights and half of the recommended number of repetitions. Those interested in gaining weight should also add one set to each exercise, with the exception of abdominal movements. The following is a good program for off-season strength improvements:

Exercise	Sets	Reps	Men	Women
1. Clean and Press	1	15-20	35%	25%
2. Jump Squats	3	15-20	40%	30%

	Sets	Reps	Men	Women
3. Leg Extension	2	15-20	25%	20%
4. Leg Curl	2	15-20	20%	15%
5. Calf Press	3-5	20-30	90%	80%
6. Bench Press	2	12-15	40%	30%
7. Bent Rowing	2	12-15	40%	30%
8. Upright Rowing	1	12-15	30%	20%
9. Reverse Curl	2	12-15	30%	20%
10. Wrist Curl	2	20-30	25%	15%
11. Reverse Wrist Curl	2	20-30	15%	10%
12. Leg Raise	1	25-100	---	---

Here is a good in-season maintenance workout to help keep up strength and bodyweight gains made with the above schedule (perform it after basketball workouts):

	Sets	Reps	Men	Women
1. Clean and Press	1	15-20	35%	25%
2. Jump Squats	1	15-20	40%	30%
3. Bench Press	1	12-15	40%	30%
4. Lat Pulldown	1	12-15	40%	30%
5. Side Laterals	1	12-15	7%	5%
6. Reverse Curl	1	12-15	30%	20%
7. Wrist Curl	1	20-30	25%	15%
8. Leg Raise	1	25-100	---	---

Bowling Program

Bowlers tend to compete in their sport year-round and have little need for an off-season program. They do, however, need leg, back, shoulder and arm strength. Here's a good training program for bowlers (it should be done at least two hours before bowling or sometime after bowling practice):

Exercise	Sets	Reps	Men	Women
1. Leg Press	2	15-20	70%	60%
2. Bent Rowing	2	8-12	40%	30%
3. Upright Rowing	1	12-15	30%	20%
4. Front Laterals	2	8-12	20%	10%
5. Dumbbell Curl	1	8-12	20%	10%
6. Back Hyperextension	1	10-20	---	---
7. Situps	1	25-100	---	---

Boxing Program

A majority of boxing trainers are opposed to weight training in the mistaken belief that such workouts will make their athletes slow or stiff. As explained in Chapter One, these beliefs are erroneous. Added strength for boxers will result in greater quickness and punching power. The following schedule should be used to supplement the usual boxing workouts:

Exercise	Sets	Reps	Men
1. Jump Squats	1	20-30	40%
2. Calf Press	2-3	30-40	90%
3. Bench Press	3-4	15-20	40%
4. Bent Rowing	2	10-15	40%
5. Military Press	2	10-15	35%
6. Upright Rowing	2	10-15	35%
7. Hanging Leg Raise	1-3	10-20	---

Canoeing/Kayaking Programs

Torso strength is essential for canoeing and kayaking. Arm strength is also important. During the winter when water workouts are impractical, canoeists and kayakers should concentrate on building strength. This program should do the trick:

Exercise	Sets	Reps	Men	Women
1. Power Snatch	1	12-15	50%	40%
2. Bent Rowing	3	8-12	40%	30%
3. Lat Pulldown Behind Neck	3	8-12	40%	30%
4. Upright Rowing	2	8-12	30%	20%
5. Side Laterals	1	12-15	10%	5%
6. Bent Laterals	1	12-15	10%	5%
7. Lat Pressdown	2	8-12	30%	20%
8. Leg Press	1	15-20	80%	70%
9. Stiff-Leg Deadlift	2	8-15	50%	40%
10. Situps	1	25-100	---	---

As the competitive season draws near, a gradual shift should be made from strength training to a very fast type of circuit training. Go directly through this program once, then repeat for a second set of each:

Flatwater kayak champion Brent Turner uses the bent-over rowing movement to strengthen his upper back muscles.

1. Upright Rowing	2	12-15	25%	15%
2. Seated Pulley Rowing	2	12-15	40%	30%
3. Front Lat Pulldown	2	12-15	40%	30%
4. Leg Press	2	15-20	70%	60%
5. Stiff-Leg Deadlift	2	8-15	45%	35%
6. Leg Raise	2	25-50	---	---
7. Bent Laterals	2	12-15	10%	5%

Crew (Rowing) Programs

The rowing stroke has two phases, each involving different muscle groups. During the pulling phase of a stroke, primary muscular emphasis is on the thighs, biceps, deltoids and both upper and lower back. During recovery, emphasis shifts to the trunk flexors and the hamstring muscles. Developing greater strength through weight training should be the top priority during the autumn and winter. I'd recommend this weekly program:

Exercise	Sets	Reps	Men	Women
1. Leg Press	3	20-30	70%	60%
2. Leg Extension	2	20-30	25%	15%
3. Leg Curl	2	20-30	20%	10%
4. Power Cleans	2	12-15	50%	40%
5. Upright Rowing	2	20-30	25%	15%
6. Lat Machine Pulldown	3	20-30	45%	35%
7. Seated Pulley Rowing	3	20-30	45%	35%
8. Stiff Leg Deadlift	1	15-20	50%	40%
9. Barbell Curl	3	15-20	30%	20%
10. Situps	1	50-100	---	---

When the peak competitive season is approaching, switch over to a circuit training schedule of three very fast trips through the following group of exercises:

1. Upright Rowing	3	20-30	25%	15%
2. Leg Press	3	20-30	70%	60%
3. Power Clean	3	12-15	50%	40%
4. Situps	3	25-50	---	---
5. Seated Pulley Row	3	20-30	45%	35%
6. Stiff Legged Deadlift	3	15-20	50%	40%
7. Lat Machine Pulldown	3	20-30	45%	35%
8. Barbell Curl	3	15-20	30%	20%
9. Leg Curl	3	20-30	20%	10%
10. Leg Extension	3	20-30	25%	15%
11. Back Hyperextension	3	20-30	---	---

Cross-Country Skiing/Snowshoeing Programs

One can prepare for these two winter sports by combining weight training with running and hill hiking or hill running. Emphasis in both snowshoeing and cross-country skiing is on leg and torso development. Here is a good schedule for pre-season conditioning:

Exercise	Sets	Reps	Men	Women
1. Leg Press	2-3	20-30	70%	60%
2. Half Squat	2-3	20-30	100%	80%
3. Leg Extension	2	20-30	35%	25%
4. Leg Curl	2	20-30	20%	15%
5. Back Hyperextension	1	12-15	---	---
6. Bent-Arm Pullover	3-4	12-15	40%	30%
7. Calf Press	3-5	25-30	90%	80%
8. Situps or Leg Raise	1	25-100	---	---

Training during the competitive or participatory season should be lighter and faster than during the off-season. One quick trip through this schedule four to six days weekly should prove effective:

Exercise	Sets	Reps	Men	Women
1. Leg Press	1	20-30	70%	60%
2. Leg Extension	1	20-30	35%	25%
3. Half Squat	1	20-30	20%	10%
4. Leg Curl	1	20-30	20%	10%
5. Bent-Arm Pullover	1	20-30	40%	30%
6. Calf Press	1	20-30	90%	80%
7. Back Hyperextension	1	12-15	---	---
8. Situps	1	25-50	---	---

Cycling Program

Cycling demands tremendous thigh, hamstring and calf strength and endurance. The following program can be performed three non-consecutive days each week both in and out of season:

Exercise	Sets	Reps	Men	Women
1. Leg Press	2-3	30-50	65%	55%
2. Step Up	2-3	20-30	30%	20%
3. Half Squat	2-3	20-30	70%	60%
4. Calf Press	3-5	30-50	80%	70%
5. Donkey Calf Raise	3-5	20-30	100%	90%

6. Leg Curl	3-4	30-50	15%	10%
7. Power Clean	1	15-20	45%	35%
8. Situps	1	25-100	---	---
9. Wrist Curls	1-3	20-30	30%	20%

Diving Program

Springboard and platform diving require a combination of agility, flexibility and strength. Weight training should be done after diving workouts, with the emphasis on leg and abdominal development. This schedule can be performed three times a week both in and out of the competitive season:

Exercise	Sets	Reps	Men	Women
1. Jump Squat	2-3	15-20	60%	50%
2. Calf Machine	3-5	20-30	100%	90%
3. Incline Situps	1-2	20-30	---	---
4. Incline Leg Raises	1-2	20-30	---	---
5. Frog Kick	1-2	15-20	---	---
6. Twisting Movement	1-2	50-100	---	---

Fencing Program

Fencers should place emphasis on the legs, as well as deltoids and arm muscles. Try the following exercises and be sure to perform them with a full range of motion:

Exercise	Sets	Reps	Men	Women
1. Squat	1	12-15	75%	65%
2. Lunge	2-3	12-15	35%	25%
3. Leg Curl	2-3	12-15	20%	10%
4. Upright Rowing	2	8-12	30%	20%
5. Bench Press	2	8-12	40%	30%
6. Military Press	2	8-12	30%	20%
7. Reverse Curl	2	8-12	20%	10%
8. Wrist Curl	2	20-30	25%	15%
9. Reverse Wrist Curl	2	20-30	15%	10%
10. Parallel Bar Leg Raise	1	10-15	---	---

Football/Rugby Programs

Football demands great power and quickness, as does the

related sport of rugby. All professional football teams and most college and high school teams stress weight training. Indeed, many of these teams have retained special "strength coaches" to ensure that their athletes have access to proper supervision. Many rugby players also train hard with heavy resistance.

Two basic types of programs are presented here for out-of-season training. This first one is for the positions which require heavy players — e.g., tackle and guard in football, prop in rugby:

Exercise	Sets	Reps	Men
1. Clean and Press	1	12-15	60%
2. Power Clean	3-5	6-8	65%
3. Deadlift	3-5	3-5	110%
4. Shoulder Shrug	3	8-12	90%
5. Bench Squat	3-5	8-12	120%
6. Leg Extension	3	8-12	60%
7. Leg Curl	3	8-12	30%
8. Bench Press	3-5	6-8	75%
9. Bent Rowing	3	8-10	70%
10. Press Behind Neck	3	6-8	50%
11. Bent-Arm Pullover	3	8-12	50%
12. Wrist Curls	3-4	15-20	40%
13. Donkey Calf Raise	5-8	15-20	100%
14. Calf Press	5-8	15-20	100%
15. Situps	1-3	25-100	---
16. Wrestler's Bridge	2-3	---	---

Players in the "lighter" positions — e.g., scrum half in rugby, flanker back in football — should profit from three days a week on this type of schedule:

1. Clean and Press	1	12-15	50%
2. Power Clean	3-5	6-8	65%
3. Stiff-Leg Deadlift	2-3	6-8	70%
4. Upright Row	2-3	8-12	35%
5. Lat Pulldown	3-5	8-12	60%
6. Jump Squat	3-5	8-12	80%
7. Leg Extension	3	8-12	60%

8. Leg Curl	3	8-12	30%
9. Bench Press	3-5	6-8	75%
10. Bent-Arm Pullover	3-4	8-12	50%
11. Press Behind Neck	3	6-8	50%
12. Barbell Curl	3	8-12	40%
13. Side Straddle Hop	5-8	15-20	100%
14. Frog Kick	1-3	15-25	---
15. Wrist Curls	3-4	15-20	40%
16. Head Strap	3-4	8-12	20%

In recent years, experiments on the value of strength training have been conducted in the National Football League. Two groups of players were compared. The first did no weight training during the course of the season, while the second trained twice each week on a moderate schedule. When the groups were compared, the lifters maintained their beginning of training camp strength for the entire season, while the non-weight-trained group lost up to 50 percent of their functional strength over the long season.

As a result of this research, most players now train with weights two or three times weekly. I would recommend one workout the day after a game and a seond three days later. The following abbreviated strength maintenance schedule should take no more than a half hour to perform and is suitable for all positions:

1. Clean and Press	1	12-15	50%
2. Power Clean	1	8-12	60%
3. Bent Rowing	1	8-12	60%
4. Stiff-Leg Deadlift	1	8-12	65%
5. Leg Press	1	20-30	120%
6. Leg Curl	1	15-20	25%
7. Bench Press	1	8-12	65%
8. Bent-Arm Pullover	1	8-12	50%
9. Press Behind Neck	1	8-12	45%
10. Barbell Curl	1	8-12	40%
11. Calf Press	1	20-30	120%
12. Side Straddle Hop	1	20-30	100%

13. Wrist Curl	1	20-30	40%
14. Incline Situps	1	25-50	---
15. Partner Neck Pressure	1	---	---

Golf Program

Golfers have been turning to weight training recently in growing numbers. The famous Gary Player is one of many great golfers who weight-train to improve their game. Golfers particularly need deltoid and forearm strength. Here is a good in-season and off-season program that should be done two or three times weekly:

Exercise	Sets	Reps	Men	Women
1. Clean and Press	1	8-12	45%	35%
2. Half Squat	2	12-15	60%	50%
3. Calf Raise	2	15-20	60%	50%
4. Bent Rowing	2	8-12	40%	30%
5. Upright Rowing	1	8-12	35%	25%
6. Bench Press	2	8-12	40%	30%
7. Stiff-Arm Pullover	1	12-15	20%	10%
8. Side Laterals	2	12-15	10%	5%
9. Bent Laterals	2	12-15	10%	5%
10. Reverse Curl	2	8-12	25%	15%
11. Wrist Curl	3	15-20	30%	20%
12. Reverse Wrist Curl	3	15-20	15%	10%
13. Seated Twisting	1	25-100	10%	10%
14. Situps	1	25-100	---	---

Gymnastics Program

The chief value of weight training for gymnastics is the improvement of chronically weak muscle groups. Any experienced coach can pick out weak muscle areas within a few minutes. Once such areas have been isolated, an athlete should choose two or three movements for that area, performing a maximum of six to eight sets for each muscle group three times weekly. Most contemporary gymnasts expend all of their workout energy training on their various types of apparatus and do not train with weights. In the event, however, that a gymnast wishes to improve overall body strength, the following schedule is recommended:

Exercise	Sets	Reps	Men	Women
1. Clean and Press	1	12-15	40%	30%
2. Jump Squats	2	12-15	50%	40%
3. Calf Press	3-4	20-30	100%	80%
4. Upright Rowing	2	8-12	35%	25%
5. Bench Press	3	8-12	50%	40%
6. Front Lat Pulldown	3	12-15	70%	60%
7. Military Press	2	8-12	55%	45%
8. Front Lateral Raise	2	12-15	25%	15%
9. Barbell Curl	2	8-12	35%	25%
10. Incline Leg Raise	1	25-50	---	---
11. Incline Situps	1	25-50	---	---

Handball Program

Many handball players — especially beginners — discover that shots with their natural hand are both stronger and more accurate than shots with the off hand. Weight training is a good way to overcome the off-hand weakness that plagues so many players. Such exercises done three or four times a week will quickly add strength to the weak hand. Here is a weight schedule that should do the trick:

Exercise	Sets	Reps	Men	Women
1. Clean and Press	1	12-15	45%	35%
2. Jump Squats	2	12-15	65%	55%
3. Leg Extension	2	15-20	40%	30%
4. Leg Curl	2	15-20	20%	15%
5. Calf Press	3-5	20-30	100%	80%
6. Lying Laterals	2	8-12	15%	10%
7. Bent Laterals	2	8-12	10%	5%
8. Standing Laterals	2	8-12	10%	5%
9. Back Hyperextension	1	10-15	---	---
10. Situps	1	25-100	---	---

Ice Hockey/Field Hockey Program

Ice and field hockey may seem dissimilar, but they have much in common insofar as muscle involvement is concerned. Both demand strength in legs, arms and shoulders. This program should improve performance in either sport:

Exercise	Sets	Reps	Men	Women
1. Clean and Press	1	12-15	45%	35%
2. Power Clean	2	8-10	55%	45%
3. Squat	2	12-15	60%	50%
4. Leg Curl	2	12-15	20%	15%
5. Upright Row	2	8-12	25%	15%
6. Bench Press	2	8-12	50%	40%
7. Lying Laterals	2	8-12	15%	10%
8. Bent Laterals	2	8-12	10%	5%
9. Side Laterals	2	8-12	10%	5%
10. Back Hyperextension	1	10-15	---	---
11. Situps	1	25-100	---	---
12. Calf Machine	5	20-30	100%	80%

Ice Skating Program

Both figure and speed skating require lower body strength with only minimal necessity for a stronger-than-average upper body. This type of schedule will develop the required lower body strength:

Exercise	Sets	Reps	Men	Women
1. Bench Press	2	8-12	50%	40%
2. Lat Pulldown	2	12-15	50%	40%
3. Bench Squat	3	12-15	100%	80%
4. Front Squat	2	12-15	80%	70%
5. Leg Extension	2	15-20	40%	30%
6. Leg Curl	2	12-15	20%	15%
7. Back Hyperextension	1	10-15	---	---
8. Bar On Knees Calf Raise	3-5	20-30	100%	90%
9. Side Bend	1	25-100	10%	10%
10. Situps	1	25-100	---	---

Lacrosse Program

That great American Indian sport of lacrosse has gained considerable popularity in recent years. Lacrosse is an activity demanding great endurance and the ability to take some punishing body contact. The following program should be done in the pre-season period. In-season, the program should be done only twice a week, with only one set of each movement.

Exercise	Sets	Reps	Men
1. Power Clean	2-3	6-10	60%
2. Squat	3	12-15	85%
3. Upright Rowing	2	8-12	40%
4. Bent Rowing	3	8-12	50%
5. Bent Laterals	2	12-15	10%
6. Bench Press	3	8-12	60%
7. Lying Laterals	2	12-15	20%
8. Press Behind Neck	3	8-12	45%
9. Front Laterals	2	12-15	20%
10. Side Straddle Hop	3-5	30-50	100%
11. Side Bend	1	25-100	10%
12. Hanging Leg Raise	1	25-100	---

Martial Arts Program

All phases of the martial arts have become very popular recently as a result of massive magazine, movie and television exposure. Judo enthusiasts have long been interested in weight training as an adjunct to their specific judo training. Recently, however, participants in all of the martial arts have been turning to progressive resistance exercise to strengthen subpar muscles and improve performance. Here is a whole-body type of weight training program suitable for all martial arts participants:

Exercise	Sets	Reps	Men	Women
1. Clean and Press	1	12-15	45%	35%
2. Leg Press	3	15-20	100%	80%
3. Leg Curl	2	15-20	20%	15%
4. Stiff-Leg Deadlift	2	8-12	60%	50%

5.	Lat Pulldown	3	12-15	50%	40%
6.	Dumbbell Bench Press	3	9-12	50%	40%
7.	Upright Rowing	2	8-12	40%	30%
8.	Military Press	2	8-12	40%	30%
9.	Seated Dumbbell Curl	2	8-12	35%	25%
10.	Lat Pressdown	2	8-12	35%	25%
11.	Wrist Curl	2	20-30	35%	25%
12.	Donkey Calf Raise	3-5	20-30	100%	80%
13.	Sidebend	1	25-100	10%	10%
14.	Twisting	1	25-100	10%	10%
15.	Situps	1	25-100	---	---

Mountain Climbing/Hiking Program

Hiking and mountain climbing are a good test of overall body strength, especially leg power. Such power can be particularly important for "weekend warrior" type hikers and climbers. This type of program can be performed three times a week before hitting the hills on weekends:

Exercise		Sets	Reps	Men	Women
1.	Clean and Press	1	12-15	45%	35%
2.	Shoulder Shrug	3	12-15	60%	50%
3.	Lat Pulldown	3	8-12	50%	40%
4.	Stiff-Leg Deadlift	1-2	8-12	60%	50%
5.	Bench Press	3	8-12	50%	40%
6.	Bent-Arm Pullovers	2-3	12-15	40%	30%
7.	Step-Up	3	15-20	50%	40%
8.	Leg Press	3	15-20	100%	80%
9.	Calf Press	3-5	20-30	100%	80%
10.	Reverse Curl	2	12-15	25%	15%
11.	Wrist Curl	2	20-30	40%	30%
12.	Frog Kick	1	15-25	---	---

Racquet Sports Program

Badminton, squash, tennis and racquetball skills can all be improved by using the same weight training schedule. Emphasis should be on leg, torso and arm strength. The following program will provide such extra strength:

Exercise	Sets	Reps	Men	Women
1. Power Snatch	1	12-15	40%	30%
2. Bench Squat	3	15-20	90%	80%
3. Leg Extension	2	12-15	40%	30%
4. Leg Curl	2	12-15	20%	15%
5. Back Hyperextension	1	10-15	---	---
6. Lying Laterals	2	8-12	30%	20%
7. Bent Laterals	2	8-12	15%	10%
8. Front Laterals	2	8-12	15%	10%
9. Side Laterals	2	8-12	15%	10%
10. Barbell Reverse Curl	2	8-12	30%	20%
11. French Press	2	8-12	35%	25%
12. Wrist Curl	3	15-20	40%	30%
13. Reverse Wrist Curl	3	15-20	20%	15%
14. Calf Press	3-5	20-30	100%	80%
15. Situps or Leg Raises	1	25-100	---	---

Skiing/Water Skiing Programs

Snow (alpine) skiing and its aquatic cousin, water skiing, require thigh power and some amount of upper body strength. Research has shown that in alpine skiing, weekend athletes are most often injured on the final run of the day, an indication that fatigue can cause or lead to injuries. Pre-season conditioning can prevent such injuries as well as first-day muscle soreness — to say nothing of improving performance. This program is suitable for recreational athletes in either skiing event:

Exercise	Sets	Reps	Men	Women
1. Leg Press	3	15-20	100%	80%
2. Leg Extension	3	15-20	40%	30%
3. Leg Curl	3	15-20	20%	15%
4. Calf Press	3-5	20-30	100%	80%
5. Bench Press	3	15-20	45%	35%
6. Lat Pulldown	3	15-20	45%	35%
7. Wrist Roller	1-2	6-10	---	---
8. Back Hyperextension	1	10-15	---	---

9. Situps	1-2	50-100	---	---
10. Leg Raises	1-2	50-100	---	---

Competitive alpine and water skiing enthusiasts can train much more intensively during the off-season and then maintain their strength during the season with the above type of schedule. Here is a good off-season program for competing athletes:

1. Clean and Press	1	12-15	40%	30%
2. Jumping Squat	3-4	12-15	60%	50%
3. Bench Squat	3-4	15-20	90%	80%
4. Leg Curl	3	15-20	20%	15%
5. Power Clean	3-5	8-12	55%	45%
6. Bent Rowing (Dumbbells)	3	8-12	50%	40%
7. Stiff-Leg Deadlift	3	15-20	60%	50%
8. Bench Press	3-5	8-12	50%	40%
9. Hanging Leg Raises	2-3	15-25	---	---
10. Sidebends	2-3	50-100	10%	10%
11. Side Straddle Hop	5-8	30-50	100%	80%

Soccer Program

Soccer football is the world's most popular sport, and has burgeoned recently in the United States. Weight training for soccer can be done three times weekly. Here is a good schedule for both in-and out-of-season workouts:

Exercise	Sets	Reps	Men	Women
1. Clean and Press	1	12-15	40%	30%
2. Leg Press	1	15-20	100%	80%
3. Leg Extension	1	15-20	40%	30%
4. Leg Curl	1	15-20	20%	15%
5. Calf Machine	2	20-30	100%	80%
6. Calf Press	2	20-30	100%	80%
7. Bent Arm Pullover	1	8-12	40%	30%
8. French Press	1	8-12	25%	15%
9. Side Bend	1	25-100	10%	10%
10. Situps	1	25-100	---	---

Swimming Program

Most champion swimmers today do some sort of progressive resistance exercise, either in the form of weight training or in the use of rubber tubing. Many more could profit from the extensive type of program used by both male and female swimmers in East Germany. They do about twice as much as is included in this program:

Exercise	Sets	Reps	Men	Women
1. Leg Press	3-4	20-30	100%	80%
2. Leg Curl	2-3	20-30	30%	20%
3. Back Hyperextension	2	10-15	---	---
4. Lat Pulldown Front	3-5	15-20	50%	40%
5. Bent-Arm Pullover	3-5	15-20	50%	40%
6. Seated Pulley Rowing	3-5	15-20	50%	40%
7. Reverse Narrow Lat Pulldown	3-5	15-20	50%	40%

A key movement for swimmers is the lat pulldown. It strengthens the upper back muscles.

	Sets	Reps	Men	Women
8. Incline Leg Raises	1-3	15-20	---	---
9. Straight Arm Pullover	3-4	.15-20	20%	15%

Track and Field Programs

Track and field consists of so many events using dissimilar muscle groups that it would be impossible to recommend an all-inclusive program which would provide maximum improvement in each event. Here we'll first outline a general program. Then we'll go through the events individually, pointing out specific exercises to be added to the general program to improve strength for each event. Here is the general program:

Exercise	Sets	Reps	Men	Women
1. Leg Press	3-4	15-20	100%	90%
2. Bench Press	3-4	8-12	50%	40%
3. Lat Pulldown	3-4	8-12	50%	40%
4. Stiff-Leg Deadlift	2-3	8-12	60%	50%
5. Upright Row	2-3	8-12	35%	25%
6. Military Press	3	6-10	40%	30%
7. Barbell Curl	3	8-12	35%	25%
8. Wrist Curl	3	15-20	35%	25%
9. Situps	1-3	25-100	---	---

Shot Put Exercises

Shot putters were the first field athletes to turn in great numbers to weight training as a supplement to their training. Basic strength is quite evident in the best bench press marks of many recent champions. Dallas Long, 1964 Olympic champion with a put of 66' 8½", was able to bench press 550 pounds, 1968 champion Randy Matson benched more than 450, George Woods more than 500, and Al Feuerbach and Brian Oldfield both more than 450.

Shot putters, both male and female, should expand the bench press section to 6-8 sets of 10-8-6-4-2-2-2-2 reps with heavier weights each set. Wrist curl sets should also be upped, to 5-8 sets. Squats can be substituted for leg presses with a 10-8-6-5-5-5-5-5 rep scheme. Heavy side bends, 3-4 sets, and heavy French presses, 3-5 sets, should also be added. The final addition is that the athlete should periodically practice the Olympic lifts of snatch, and clean and jerk, both in the squat style. Feuerbach has jerked in excess of 430 pounds, as have Sam Walker and Ron Semkiw (the latter threw 70 feet in the shot put at 19 years of age!). Olympic-style wieghtlifting— commonly called Olympic lifting — is also appropriate for women shot putters, although few currently train in that manner.

Discus Exercises

Virtually all current discus throwers also weight train. Bench presses should be expanded to the shot put program's 6-8 sets of 10-8-6-4-2-2-2-2, while squats should be substituted for leg presses with 5-7 sets of 5 reps as a goal. Bent-arm laterals on a flat bench, 3-5 sets of 6-8 reps, and heavy twisting movements, 3-5 sets of 15-25 reps, should be added. Expand the wrist curls to 5 sets, with an additional 3-5 sets of dumbell wrist curls.

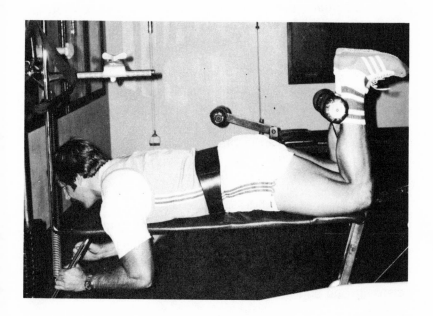

Hammer Throw Exercises

The two-hand squat snatch and the squat-style clean and jerk are key exercises for hammer throwers and can be done two or three times weekly. Hammer throwers should omit the leg presses and concentrate on 5-7 sets of 5-6 reps in the front squat. Add 2-3 sets of heavy twists with 12-20 reps and 4-6 sets of barbell shrugs in low reps of 6-8. Substitute 5 sets of bent-over rowing, 6-10 reps, for the lat pulldowns and increase the stiff-legged deadlifts to 5-6 sets.

Javelin Throw Exercises

I have had considerable personal experience with weight training for the javelin, having increased my best throw once from 196 feet to 228 feet in three months by only increasing strength (through weight training) and adding a bit of body-weight (five to six pounds). Bent-arm pullovers in sets of 5-8, working up to 12 reps with 255 pounds, formed the nucleus of the program. Weighted situps (3-5 sets, 6-12 reps), weighted twists (2-3 sets, 15-25 reps), wrist rollers (3-5 times each way for a maximum effort) were also included. Add these exercises to the basic track and field schedule to build the specific strength necessary for javelin throwing.

Long Jump/Triple Jump Exercises

Horizontal jumpers should add step-ups and jumping squats (both 3-5 sets, 12-15 reps) to the basic schedule. Cut back exercises 2-8 to only one or two sets each. Plenty of calf work can be added to the end of the basic program. This calf work should take the form of donkey calf raises and side straddle hops (both 4-5 sets, 20-30 reps).

High Jump Exercises

High jumpers, regardless of what style they use, need great thigh and calf strength. Like horizontal jumpers, they should add step-ups and jumping squats, each performed for 3-5 sets of 12-15 reps. They should cut back exercises 2-8 to one or two sets each, and add four to five sets, 20-30 reps, of both donkey calf raises and side straddle hops. High jumpers can also substitute bench squats for leg presses.

Pole Vault Exercises

In addition to the leg strength of a sprinter, pole vaulters need very strong upper bodies. They should add leg extensions and leg curls, both performed for 2-3 sets of 12-15 reps. About 4-5 sets, 20-30 reps of the calf press can be done. Lat pulldowns should be changed to overgrip front chins with added resistance tied around the waist. The number of sets of exercises 5-6 can be increases. Bench presses must be increased to 12-10-8-6-4-2-1 reps with heavier weights each set. An effort should be made to lift generally heavier weights in all other exercises.

Sprints/Hurdles Exercises

Hurdlers and sprinters can do the entire basic program

Donna Valaitis, Canadian middle-distance runner, demonstrates the shoulder shrug movement.

three days each week with the addition of 1-3 sets, 15-20 reps of step-ups, leg curls, and leg extensions, and 5-8 sets, 20-30 reps of the side straddle hop. Related resistance exercises include running up hills or stadium steps and running with a heavy object dragging behind or with a training partner holding the athlete back.

Endurance Running/Race Walking Exercises

Distance runners and race walkers put in so many training miles that they seldom need any weight training exercises for the lower body. Many do, however, tend to tie up in their upper bodies during a race, a condition which could be eliminated with the following simple program (do not rest between sets):

Exercise	Sets	Reps	Men	Women
1. Clean and Press	1	15-20	30%	20%
2. Bent Rowing	1	15-20	30%	20%
3. Barbell Curl	1	15-20	30%	20%
4. Military Press	1	15-20	30%	20%
5. Upright Rowing	1	15-20	30%	20%
6. Lat Pulldown	1	15-20	40%	30%
7. Situps (bent knees)	1	25-50	---	---

Decathlon/Pentathlon Program

Most decathletes and pentathletes have recognized the value of heavy weight training to develop extra overall body strength. The following program done out of season and three to four times weekly should drastically improve such strength:

Exercise	Sets	Reps	Men	Women
1. Clean and Press	1	12-15	50%	40%
2. Power Clean	3-4	6-8	70%	60%
3. Bent Rowing	3-4	6-8	60%	50%
4. Bent-Arm Pullover	3-4	6-8	50%	40%
5. Bench Press	5-7	6-8	60%	50%
6. Press Behind Neck	2-3	6-10	50%	40%
7. Barbell Curl	2-3	6-10	45%	35%
8. Bench Squat	3-5	15-20	100%	80%
9. Leg Curl	2-3	15-20	20%	15%

	Sets	Reps		
10. Calf Press	5-8	20-30	100%	80%
11. Wrist Curl	2-3	15-20	40%	30%
12. Incline Situps	1-3	15-20	---	---

Water Polo Program

Pete Cutino, coach of three recent NCAA champion water polo teams at the University of California and two AAU champion teams from the Concord Swim Club, considers weight training essential for water polo players. Cutino particularly recommends triceps, leg and pulling strength development exercises for his teams. Here is a schedule that emphasizes these types of exercises:

Exercise	Sets	Reps	Men
1. Power Clean	2-3	6-8	50%
2. Bench Press	3-5	8-10	60%
3. Military Press	2-3	6-10	40%
4. Standing French Press	3	8-12	35%
5. Lat Machine Pressdown	3	8-12	35%
6. Bench Squat	3-5	15-20	100%
7. Leg Press	3-5	15-20	100%
8. Leg Curl	3-5	15-20	30%
9. Front Lat Pulldown	3	12-15	60%
10. Upright Rowing	3	8-12	40%
11. Bent-Arm Pullover	2-3	12-15	45%
12. Parallel Bar Leg Raise	1-3	15-25	---

Wrestling Programs

Wrestling is one of man's oldest sports. As mentioned earlier, Milo of Crotona, the first weight-trained athlete, was a wrestler. Both free-style and Greco-Roman wrestling demand overall body strength with emphasis on neck, chest, shoulders and upper back. A good three-day-per-week workout during the off-season would look like this:

Exercise	Sets	Reps	Men
1. Power Snatch	2-3	6-8	45%
2. Jumping Squats	3-4	12-15	60%
3. Bench Press	3-5	8-12	75%

4.	Upright Row	3	8-12	45%
5.	Military Press	3	6-10	50%
6.	Lat Pulldown Behind Neck	3	12-15	60%
7.	Dumbbell Bent Rowing	3	8-12	60%
8.	Shoulder Shrug	3	15-20	90%
9.	Good Mornings	2-3	15-20	30%
10.	Barbell Curl	3-5	8-12	45%
11.	Wrist Curl	3-5	15-20	40%
12.	Hanging Leg Raise	2-3	10-25	---

Wrestling practice will take up most of an athlete's workout time during the competitive season, but the following abbreviated program done with no rest between sets will help to maintain a high strength level:

1.	Clean and Press	1	8-12	60%
2.	Leg Press	1	15-20	100%
3.	Bench Press	1	8-12	75%
4.	Front Lat Pulldown	1	8-12	60%
5.	Shrug	1	15-20	90%
6.	Bent-Arm Pullover	1	10-12	50%
7.	Good Mornings	1	15-20	35%
8.	Barbell Curl	1	8-12	45%
9.	Military Press	1	6-10	50%
10.	Parallel Bar Leg Raise	1	10-25	---

Wrist Wrestling Program

Wrist wrestling for men and women is gaining popularity throughout the United States. What was once a male test of strength in Army barracks and beer halls is now an organized sport, with national and world championships which receive considerable television coverage. A good supplementary weight training schedule for wrist wrestlers would stress upper body strength. Here is a good program for wrist wrestlers:

	Exercise	Sets	Reps	Men	Women
1.	Bench Press	5-8	4-6	90%	75%
2.	Bent-Arm Laterals	3-5	6-8	30%	20%
3.	Bent-Arm Pullover	3-5	8-12	50%	40%

4. Seated Press Behind Neck	3-5	5-8	55%	45%
5. Barbell Curl	3	8-10	45%	35%
6. Reverse Curl	3-5	8-10	35%	25%
7. Wrist Curl	3-5	15-20	40%	30%
8. Reverse Wrist Curls	3-5	15-20	20%	15%
9. Back Hyperextension	1	12-20	---	---
10. Situps	1	25-100	---	---

Volleyball Program

The primary advantage of weight training for volleyball is the improvement of vertical jumping ability. An increase of six inches is entirely possible within a two-to three-month period with proper weight training. Here is a good volleyball schedule for both in and out of season:

Exercise	Sets	Reps	Men	Women
1. Clean and Press	1	12-15	40%	30%
2. Jumping Squats	2-3	12-15	60%	50%
3. Bench Squat	2-3	12-15	100%	80%
4. Calf Press	3-5	15-20	100%	80%
5. Side Straddle Hop	3-5	20-30	50%	40%
6. Front Lat Pulldown	2-3	12-15	45%	35%
7. Lat Pressdown	2-3	10-12	30%	20%
8. Military Press	2-3	6-10	40%	30%
9. Back Hyperextension	1	12-20	---	---
10. Situps	1	25-100	---	---

Summary

Each of these recommended weight training schedules is only as good as you make it. Missing workouts or not pushing up your training poundages will not bring full strength improvement. Suggested starting poundages, again, are approximate and may need to be adjusted either up or down. Ideally, with the correct training poundage the final one or two reps of each set will be difficult but not impossible to complete.

5

Bodybuilding And Competitive Weightlifting

As mentioned in Chapter One, there are a significant number of men competing in the sports of powerlifting, Olympic weightlifting and bodybuilding. In recent years a small number of women have been entering the lighter classes at weightlifting meets, but to date none have entered male physique contests. Many do, however, enter figure perfection contests which exist as the female equivalent of male physique competitions.

How To Watch A Weightlifting Meet

Competitions in what the uninitiated call weightlifting are divided by the true aficionado into Olympic lifting, power-lifting and bodybuilding championships. In each of these three divisions, meets are held on local, state, district, national and international levels. Although competitions are held under AAU and other auspices in each of these sports year-round, the peak season in the United States runs from November or December through the middle of June.

Olympic-style weightlifting is the oldest of the three Iron

Game sports, the first national championships having been held in 1928 at Philadelphia. Five different lifts were contested: the one-hand snatch, one-hand clean and jerk, two-hand military press, two-hand snatch and two-hand clean and jerk. Since only the three two-hand lifts were used at the Olympic Games, the one-hand exercises were soon dropped and the press, snatch and the clean and jerk were contested in the United States through the 1972 Olympics. At that point the international federation for Olympic lifting voted to drop the press movement because it had become difficult to officiate. Thus the current two-event program of snatch and clean and jerk is contested both domestically and internationally.

World supremacy in Olympic lifting has shifted many times. During the 1930s, Egypt and Germany alternated winning team titles at the World Championships. During World War II there were no international meets, but American athletes were able to forge ahead because the many lifters who stayed in the US were far from the war zone and able to train. Their European and Asian counterparts, who had the war in their backyards, were not as fortunate. As a result, the United States was on top of world rankings from about 1946 to 1960. Since the 1960 Rome Olympics until the present, however, the Soviet Union has consistently ruled international Olympic lifting despite challenges from Poland, Japan and lately Bulgaria.

Olympic-style weightlifting demands every quality of an athlete: speed, flexibility, coordination, exceptional strength and, to some extent, endurance. So in addition to long workouts with barbells, weightlifters train in a variety of other sports including running, gymnastics, soccer, volleyball and basketball. Such an eclectic approach to workouts has produced some lifts which verge on the unbelievable. Soviet super-heavyweight Vasili Alexeev, for example, snatches nearly 420 pounds and jerks about 540. The average person could not lift one end of a 540-pound barbell off the floor!

There are nine weight classes in weightlifting meets. Due to international affiliations, the class limits are in kilos, but to the nearest pound they are 114, 123, 132, 148, 165, 181, 198, 242

In the lighter weightlifting classes, athletes tend to be very trim. Here John Raffaele snatches 297 at a bodyweight of 181.

and unlimited or super-heavyweight. At national and some lesser meets athletes lift kilo barbell sets. However, barbells graduated in pounds are still used at most American competitions.

The snatch is the first lift contested in each meet. It consists of lifting a barbell from the floor to locked arms' length overhead in one motion, with no stops en route. Usually a wide grip is used and the lifter can either squat or split his legs fore and aft suddenly to lower the body once the barbell has reached its peak altitude. This lowering of the body compensates for inability to pull very heavy weights more than a few feet from the platform. Once the weight has been fixed overhead, the athlete must stand up with it and hold steady with feet on a line for a period of about two seconds. Finally the referee signals "down" and the lift is complete.

The clean and jerk consists of hoisting the barbell from the floor to the same finish position as for the snatch, but in two movements and with a narrower grip. The clean portion is from floor to shoulders in one motion while squatting or splitting under the weight. The lifter then comes erect, "gathers his

Many women are entering weightlifting meets. Meridy Schmidt actually won a state championship while lifting against men. The weight on the bar is 60 kilos (132 pounds).

psych," dips his body slightly, rams the bar upward as high as possible with leg strength and splits to fix the weight. He recovers by bringing his feet together, waits for the count and lowers the bar back to the floor. The barbell can be dropped at the completion of either lift, but recent rule changes now require both hands to remain on the bar to guide it evenly back to the platform. It should also be noted that most athletes consider psychological preparation to be 75 percent of the battle in weightlifting and powerlifting.

Three graduated attempts are allowed in each of the two lifts. Between first attempt and second, a minimum increase (or jump) of 10 pounds (or five kilos) must be taken, while between second and third attempts the minimum jump is five pounds (2½ kilos). The winner of the competition is determined by adding up the best successful attempt of each lift. In the event of a tie, the lighter individual wins, as he has lifted more in proportion to his bodyweight. Often one's bodyweight will determine strategy as a meet goes down to the last two or three lifts. As an example, if two evenly matched lifters are of different bodyweight, the lighter man need choose his final attempts only to tie, while the heavier man must actually beat his opponent by a minimum of 2½ kilos (or five pounds).

The AAU holds Junior National Championships in May of each year and Senior National Championships in June. The World Championships are held in September or October, or in August during Olympic years. Each of these competitions also includes a team title computed by assigning graduated points for each of the first six finishers in every class.

Powerlifters compete in three lifts: the squat, bench press and deadlift. The sport became popular in the United States about 20 years ago, but was not organized on a national level until about 10 years ago. Junior and Senior Nationals are held annually, as well as World Championships. The sport is still in its infancy, however, and international meets are not yet truly representative.

Powerlift meets are held in 10 bodyweight classes (in powerlifting there is an extra class with a limit of 100 kilos or

220 pounds). Rules for scoring and number of attempts are the same as for Olympic lifts. Monstrous poundages are lifted — 900-pound squats, 650-pound bench presses and 850-pound deadlifts becoming common.

The squat is the first lift to be contested in a powerlifting meet. The athlete approaches a weighted barbell which rests on a pair of stands. Racking the weight behind his head and across his shoulders, he steps back and does a deep knee bend. At the deepest point of this movement, the upper thigh must go below an imaginary line parallel to the floor before the athlete recovers to starting position and places the bar back on its stands.

When doing a competitive bench press, the athlete lies back on a bench and starts with the barbell at straight arms' length over the chest. The weight is lowered to mid-chest and

Extremely heavy weights can be handled in the deadlift, the third of the power lifts. Here Paul Love has 600 pounds almost at the finish position.

held for one second. As soon as the referee claps, the bar is pressed back to starting position. A grip width limit of slightly over 30 inches has been imposed, and hips or feet cannot be shifted from bench or floor during the progress of the lift.

The deadlift is the simplest of the three exercises in that the barbell is lifted from the floor to a position across the upper thighs with the legs locked, torso upright and shoulders pulled back. The main causes for disqualification are: 1) stopping the bar somewhere along its upward path; or 2) "hitching" it up the thighs ("hitching" involves using the thighs as an incline up which the bar can be slid, making the lift much easier, of course).

The third Iron Game sport is competitive bodybuilding. To the average person, bodybuilders look like strutting peacocks with many pounds of useless muscle. In reality, however, most are highly conditioned athletes who train two to five hours each day. The sport is very well organized both at home and abroad and is gaining a new measure of public respectability.

The Mr. America and Mr. USA titles are the most coveted in the United States, while Mr. World, Mr. Universe and Mr. Olympia enjoy the highest degree of international prestige. State and local contests are also held in profusion.

A standard physique contest includes an award for the title winner (as well as the first three to five places) and a trophy for the Most Muscular Man. Often subdivisions for Best Arms, Abdominals, Legs, Back and Chest are contested. Occasionally, a trophy is also presented to the Best Poser. In some contests bodybuilders are divided into two or three height classes, but usually the little guys can compete on an equal basis with the 6½ footers.

Five or more judges are used and they observe each contestant's posing routine to decide on a winner. They look

Steve Reeves, Mr. America, Mr. World and Mr. Universe, is considered almost a god in bodybuilding circles. He played in a number of "Hercules" films during the early 1960s. (Photo by Russ Warner)

for an ideal combination of muscle size, shape, muscularity (absence of fat), symmetry (the proportionate relationship of one body part to another), and general appearance. Points are awarded in each category to determine overall placings. The winners of prestigious physique contests enjoy almost godlike status among devotees of the sport.

How To Become An Olympic Lifter

Any reasonably athletic youth can become a champion weightlifter if he/she is willing to work at the sport with dedication and consistency (yes, women, too, have recently begun competing in both Olympic-style and power lifting). Strength, flexibility, coordination and speed can be systematically developed over time, and usually only injury or ceasing workouts will keep one from eventually reaching championship caliber. Essentially, it's only a matter of hard work.

Blair Kephart cleans over 400 pounds in a regional competition.

Speaking idealistically, the best time to start training as an Olympic-style lifter would be at about age 15. The first year of workouts should be spent bodybuilding and participating in gymnastics, track, basketball and other agility and speed sports. This type of early training will build a solid foundation of overall body strength, speed and flexibility, all prerequisites for becoming a top level international weightlifter.

Once strength levels have been built up to the point where an athlete can squat 150 percent of bodyweight and deadlift 200 percent, it's time to gradually switch schedules from strict body power training to Olympic lift workouts. This is the type of power program that a novice might be using at the switchover point (three days a week):

1. Squat: 6 sets of 12-10-8-6-4-2 reps with added weight each set.
2. Deadlift: 5 sets of 5 reps with added weight each set.
3. Shoulder Shrug: 3 sets, 8-12 reps.
4. Bench Press: 3-5 sets, 6-8 reps.
5. Incline Situps: 2-3 sets, 20-30 reps.

At this point a maximum single effort on the squat and deadlift should be done every 14 days, the squat done one day and deadlift the next. Plenty of flexibility work should be included along with the previously mentioned sports. Concentrate on shoulder, hamstring/lower back, knee and ankle suppleness.

When changing over to Olympic lifts, the first new development should be the inclusion of power snatches and power cleans in your routine. Substitute them for deadlifts, and alternate the two each training session for five sets of five with heavy resistance. These movements are faster and much more dynamic than deadlifts and, of course, develop the same muscles. Try to get an experienced lifter to check out your form. If this isn't possible, be very careful to closely examine the photos included in the exercise pool chapter.

After one or two months of five sets of five on power snatches and cleans, start on a 5-4-3-2-1 rep scheme with heavier poundages each set in an effort to accelerate strength gains. At

The jerk starts from a standing position. The knees are dipped to throw the bar overhead, and the legs are split fore and aft to fix the bar at arms length. The feet must be brought into line to complete the lift.

this point, you should also begin to practice form on the complete lifts, again preferably under the watchful eye of an experienced lifter. Usually the jerk is easiest to learn, followed by the clean and then the snatch. Although many lifters learn the split style of lifting first and later switch to the squat method, I am convinced that it's better to squat from the start.

When first learning the lifts, use only an unloaded bar and then gradually start to add plates as the movements become more familiar to you. Also begin to include front squats every other workout in place of a back squat workout. Front squats are identical to coming up from the squat clean position with a heavy weight. Continue the flexibility exercises and participation in other sports. Once you get up to heavy poundages with the Olympic lifts, your workout might look like this (three times a week):

1. Snatch or Clean and Jerk: 8 sets, 5-4-3-2-1-2-3-4-5 reps.
2. Power Clean or Power Snatch: 3-5 sets, 5 reps.
3. Squat or Front Squat: 6 sets, 12-10-8-6-4-2 reps.
4. Shrug: 3-5 sets, 8-12 reps.
5. Back Hyperextension: 2-3 sets, 8-12 reps.
6. Weighted Situps: 2-3 sets, 8-12 reps.

From this point it is just a matter of systematically increasing exercise weights over a long period of time, and gradually increasing the work load by adding sets, exercises and even the number of workouts each week until it is up to five or six weekly. It is also a good idea to include a great deal of variety in each workout in order to keep up interest. Include high pulls occasionally as an assistance movement (one that is different from the competitive lift, but which trains the same muscles). It's not in the exercise pool chapter, so I'll describe a high pull. Use either a wide grip (as in snatching) or a narrower grip (as in the clean) and a poundage about 20 percent higher than your best single in each of those lifts. Then with good body mechanics, pull the bar as high as possible in sets of three to five reps. This movement helps build more power in your pull due to the use of heavier weights.

The jerk phase of the clean and jerk is also not included in the exercise pool since it's specialized and not the type of movement that is done with other physical activities. The real key to good jerking ability is to have the bar in a solidly supported (lifters say "racked") position across your upper chest and shoulders. Rest it securely across your deltoids with elbows held up. With a solid rack, dip your legs about six inches and ram the bar as high as possible. It's important during this dip to keep your torso perfectly upright. There is a natural tendency to lean a bit forward as you dip, which will cause you to throw the bar out in front, making it impossible to complete the lift. The bar must be rammed directly up, or a heavy weight will be difficult to fix. A straight line must be maintained from the middle of your hips up through the torso and arms to the weight. At any rate, as soon as the bar has been rammed aloft, split suddenly with your legs fore and aft to lower your body under the weight. This sudden split should allow you to fix the bar at straight arms' length overhead before the bar begins to descend. Bring your feet back on a line and you've completed a clean and jerk.

As weights get heavier and heavier in your workout it will become necessary to somehow reinforce your grip. This can be done either with straps or by using a hooked grip. Here's a series of photos illustrating how to use straps:

By reinforcing your grip with straps cut from military webbing, you will be able to lift much heavier weights than you could with only your normal grip.

Straps can be used in workouts but not in actual competition. To reinforce your grip at a meet, try hooking your grip like this:

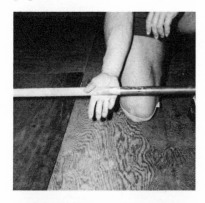 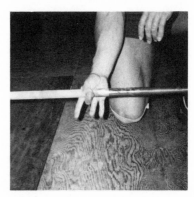

Try reinforcing your thumb by wrapping your fingers around it. This technique takes practice, but it results in a much more secure grip in competition.

With this grip you can overcome thumb weakness which often leads to a lift failure. Hooking your grip will be a bit painful at first, but in a short time will feel both comfortable and extremely secure. Personally, I can't lift a heavy weight without a hooked grip.

Once you have reached a fairly high level of competition as an Olympic-style lifter, you might be training on a schedule like this:

Monday

1. Squat Snatch: 5-7 sets, 2 reps, up to 85% of best

   2. Clean Grip High Pull: 4-5 sets, 5 reps, 120% of best clean

   3. Front Squat: 6-8 sets, 5 reps, 80%

   4. Good Morning Exercise: 3-5 sets, 6-8 reps, 60%

Tuesday

   1. Bench Press: 5 sets, 6-8 reps, 75%

   2. Shrug: 5 sets, 8-12 reps, 80%

   3. Barbell Curl: 3-5 sets, 8 reps

   4. Back Hyperextensions: 3-5 sets, 12-15 reps

   5. Incline Situps: 2-3 sets, 20-30 reps

Wednesday

   1. Squat Clean: 5-7 sets, 2 reps up to 85%

   2. Back Squat: 5-7 sets, 5 reps, 80%

   3. Power Snatch: 3-5 sets, 5 reps, 50%

   4. Hanging Leg Raises: 1-2 sets, 12-15 reps

Thursday

   1. Same as Tuesday, but substitute jerks with weight taken from a squat rack in place of the bench presses.

Friday

   1. Rest.

Saturday

   1. Work up to 90%-100% of best snatch and clean and jerk.

   2. Go 90% on one and 100% on the other alternate Saturdays.

How To Become A Powerlifter

Most powerlifters start out as bodybuilders. After a few workouts, or sometimes several years, they develop a taste for using very heavy weights and soon they are power training and not worrying about how they look. Generally speaking, powerlifting takes less athletic ability than Olympic-style lifting. Only strength and a minimum of coordination count, with flexibility, speed and endurance relatively unimportant. Power lifts are also far easier to learn than Olympic lifts.

The three power lifts are described in the exercise pool in Chapter Three and in the introductory section of this chapter. There are, however, a few tips to good performance that have not yet been discussed. The best squatters tend to rest the bar relatively low on the upper back instead of high on the neck. Good squatters also tend to use a slightly wider than shoulder width foot stance as this involves hips and thighs to the best mechanical advantage. Quality bench pressing technique is a matter of forcing the elbows back and then moving the bar slowly back over the head as the bar goes up. Some find it easier to get the barbell past the "sticking point" if they exhale as the bar slows down. This changes chest leverage geometry and often results in a completed lift which otherwise might have failed. The only secret to good deadlifting is getting a very tight reversed hook grip. You can also experiment with different starting stances as you get more experience.

Beginning powerlifters can probably make steady progress for at least a year on this kind of program:

1. Bench Press: 5-8 sets, 1-5 reps.
2. Squat: 5-8 sets, 3-5 reps.
3. Deadlift: 5-8 sets, 3-5 reps (once each week only).

To keep up interest on such a schedule, try varying reps with each workout. One you might try with 5 sets of 5, another 6 sets of 3, and maybe a third 7-8 sets of singles with progressively heavier poundages. Don't go to singles more than once every 10 days to two weeks, as going too heavy too often is an easy way to go stale. You can also try a pyramid schedule like 5-4-3-2-1-2-3-4-5 with increasing and then decreasing poundages.

Once past the novice stage, continued progress can be made by including assistance exercises, or substitutes for the actual competitive lifts. Here is a list of assistance exercises for each lift:

Squat

1. Front Squat
2. Leg Press
3. Partial Squat
4. Bench Squat
5. Leg Extension

Bench Press

1. Dumbbell Bench Press
2. Barbell or Dumbbell Incline Press
3. Barbell or Dumbbell Decline Press
4. Military Press
5. Parallel Bar Dips
6. All Triceps Exercises
7. Bent-Arm Laterals

Deadlift

1. Partial Deadlifts (off blocks of varying heights)
2. Stiff-Leg Deadlifts
3. Back Hyperextensions
4. Good Mornings

Combining these assistance movements with the actual competitive lifts, a champion powerlifter might be training like this:

Monday

1. Bench Press: 5-8 sets, 1-3 reps
2. Bent-Arm Laterals: 5 sets, 6-8 reps
3. Lying French Press: 5-8 sets, 6-8 reps

Tuesday

1. Squat: 5-8 sets, 3-5 reps
2. Leg Extensions: 4-5 sets, 8-12 reps
3. Partial Deadlifts: 6-8 sets, 1-3 reps
4. Back Hyperextensions: 3-5 sets, 8-12 reps

Wednesday

1. Incline Press: 5-8 sets, 3-5 reps
2. Parallel Bar Dips: 3-5 sets, 6-8 reps
3. Incline French Press: 5-8 sets, 6-8 reps

Thursday

1. Front Squat: 5-8 sets, 5 reps
2. Good Mornings: 3-5 sets, 8-12 reps

   3. Incline Situps: 2-3 sets, 15-25 reps
   4. Shrugs: 3-5 sets, 8-10 reps

Saturday

   1. Squat: singles up to 90-100%
   2. Bench Press: singles up to 90-100%
   3. Deadlift: singles up to 90-100%

Pat Neve won the Mr. USA title in 1974. Before he turned to bodybuilding, Pat held the world record for the bench press at 467½ pounds while weighing only 180.

How To Become A Bodybuilder

Bodybuilders start out at the same point as any other beginner and then gradually increase the volume and intensity of training to stimulate their muscles more thoroughly each workout. They are very careful to train every section of the body in order to retain symmetrical proportions. And when a particular bodypart lags behind others, they will specialize on that bodypart by training it longer and harder in an effort to force it into accelerated growth.

Here is a sample program for novice bodybuilders (work out three times each week):

1. Squats: 4 sets, 12-15 reps
2. Leg Curls: 3 sets, 8-12 reps
3. Bent Rowing: 3 sets, 8-10 reps
4. Upright Rowing: 3 sets, 8-12 reps
5. Bench Press: 4 sets, 6-8 reps
6. Press Behind Neck: 3 sets, 6-8 reps
7. Dumbbell Curl: 3 sets, 8-12 reps.
8. Lat Pressdown: 3 sets, 8-12 reps
9. Wrist Curls: 4 sets, 15-20 reps
10. Calf Machine: 4-6 sets, 20-30 reps
11. Incline Situps: 1-3 sets, 15-25 reps

After three or four months, a bodybuilder can begin training on a split routine (described in detail in Chapter Seven) in order to begin building a gradually larger volume of sets. At first four sessions per week will be enough, but a few months later five per week and then six can be undertaken. Here is a representative intermediate split routine (note how many more sets are done in a week):

Monday-Wednesday-Friday

1. Bench Press: 5 sets, 6-8 reps
2. Incline Press: 4 sets, 6-8 reps
3. Parallel Bar Dips: 4 sets, 10-15 reps
4. Press Behind Neck: 5 sets, 6-8 reps
5. Side Laterals: 4 sets, 12-15 reps

6. Bent Laterals: 4 sets, 12-15 reps
7. Incline French Press: 4 sets, 8-12 reps
8. Lat Pressdown: 3 sets, 8-12 reps
9. Dumbbell Kickback: 3 sets, 8-12 reps
10. Wrist Curl: 5-8 sets, 15-25 reps
11. Calf Machine: 5-10 sets, 15-25 reps
12. Leg Raises: 2-3 sets, 25-50 reps

Pat Neve does lateral raises to build his deltoid muscles. Like most bodybuilders, Pat trains very hard, perhaps harder than athletes in other sports.

Tuesday-Thursday-Saturday

1. Squat: 5 sets, 8-15 reps
2. Leg Extension: 4 sets, 12-15 reps
3. Leg Curl: 4 sets, 12-15 reps
4. Shrug: 5 sets, 8-12 reps
5. Lat Pulldown: 5 sets, 8-12 reps
6. Bent Rowing: 4 sets, 8-12 reps
7. Bent-Arm Pullovers: 4 sets, 8-12 reps
8. Stiff-Leg Deadlift: 4 sets, 6-8 reps
9. Barbell Curl: 4 sets, 8-10 reps

Dale Adrian posing for his win at the 1975 Mr. America contest. He also won a trophy for having the best leg development.

10. Incline Curl: 3 sets, 8-12 reps
11. Concentration Curl: 3 sets, 10-15 reps
12. Donkey Calf Raise: 5-10 sets, 15-25 reps
13. Situps: 2-3 sets, 25-50 reps

On this type of schedule, one can make fairly steady gains without overtraining. It should be noted that most veteran bodybuilders would be satisfied with a gain of only five or six pounds a year. Bodies, like Rome, aren't built in a day.

Advanced bodybuilders gradually increase the total number of sets in their workouts. They also make these training sessions more intense by using a technique called supersets. This involves doing two consecutive exercises for the same bodypart with no rest between the exercises. After each superset, a short rest is taken and then the series is repeated. Some advanced men take supersets one step beyond by doing trisets of three consecutive movements.

At the 1975 AAU Mr. America contest, I interviewed 12 of the top 15 place winners in an effort to determine which elements of their training allowed these men to build such outstanding physiques. The common element, I found, were very fast-paced workouts with maximum poundages at all times. Everyone used a six-day-per-week split routine and trained between two and three hours each day.

My good friend Dale Adrian won the 1975 Mr. America title and gave me one of the exact training schedules he used in preparation for his victory—

Monday-Wednesday-Friday

Chest	Sets	Reps	Weight
1. Incline Press	4-8	6-10	200-275
2. Krusher	4-8	10-15	---
3. Decline Press	4-8	6-10	300-365
4. Weighted Dips	4-8	8-12	100-125
5. Incline Dumbbell Press	4	10	110-125
6. Bent-Arm Laterals	4	10-15	65-75
7. Bench Press	4	6-8	345-400
8. Krusher	4	15	---

Back

1. Front Pulldowns	6-10	10	200
2. Pulley Rowing	6-10	10	200
3. Back Pulldowns	5-8	8-10	225
4. Barbell Rowing	5-8	6-8	185-225
5. Shoulder Shrug	5-8	6-10	250-300
6. Back Hyperextension	5-8	20	50

Shoulders

1. Seated Press	6-8	8-12	200-225
2. Standing Laterals	6-8	10-15	45
3. Press Behind Neck	6-8	10	175-210
4. Bent Laterals	6-8	10	50
5. Upright Rowing	4	10	150
6. Front Laterals	4	10	50-60

Forearms

1. Wrist Curls	10-20	15	---

Waist

1. Situps	4-8	50-100	---
2. Leg Raises	4-8	50-100	---

Calves

1. Calf Machine	10-20	30-50	300-500
2. Toe Press	10-20	25-35	400-500

Tuesday-Thursday-Saturday

Biceps

1. Incline Curls	6-8	8-10	75-80
2. Barbell Curls	6-8	8-10	160-175
3. Dumbbell Curls	6-8	8-10	80-85
4. Preacher Bench Curls	6-8	6-8	135-150
5. Pulley Curls	4-7	8-10	150
6. Reverse Curls	4-7	10	120-125

Triceps

1. Lat Pushdowns	6-10	10-15	130
2. French Press	6-10	10-12	125-150

3. Narrow Bench Press	4-7	8-12	250
4. Close Grip Bench Dips	4-7	12-15	125
5. Dumbbell Kickbacks	4-7	10	80-85
6. Pulley Kickbacks	4-7	10	120

Thighs

1. Hack Squats	6-10	10-20	300
2. Squats	6-10	10-20	300-325
3. Leg Extension	8-10	15-20	250
4. Sissy Squats	8-10	20	---
5. Leg Curls	4-8	15-25	150

Calves
Forearms
Waist

By working fast, Dale could finish either half of the split routine in about 2½-3 hours. This schedule, he cautions, is definitely not for beginners or even intermediates. It takes years to build up a body to the point where it can make gains on this type of program. It is so long and intense that Dale often would train twice a day. The largest part of his routine was done in the morning and the calves, forearms and waist exercised each evening. The range of sets, reps and weights is variable because each depended on how Dale felt during a particular workout. If he was particularly energetic, he would train very heavy, but if he was on a down energy day, his workouts tended to be shorter and lighter. Either way it's pretty heavy schedule, but one that certainly resulted in a big win.

Dale Adrian's workouts are mind boggling, to say the least, but they are typical of modern day bodybuilders. This type of workout, however, is not applicable to the average person, so the next chapter will deal with fitness workouts for these individuals.

6

Fitness And Improvement Programs

In the last two chapters we have been concerned with weight training programs for competitive athletes, either weight-lifting/bodybuilding enthusiasts, or athletes who desire to improve their performance in other sports. Athletes make up only a small percentage of all weight trainees, however, so this chapter will deal with the remainder, those individuals who use weights for physical fitness or for physical self-improvement.

Fitness Training

Weight training can be used very successfully in conjunction with an aerobic workout program to build rugged all-round physical fitness. (Aerobics — which means "with oxygen" — refers to continuous exercise of moderate intensity, which injects a steady flow of oxygen into the body.) Aerobic activities of themselves are absolutely tremendous for health and longevity. They stimulate the heart and circulatory system, burn up excess body fat and help to relieve life's daily tensions.

But most aerobic activities will build little overall body strength.

Before discussing weight training programs for fitness, I would like to recommend several types of aerobic workouts. Physiologists have determined that in order to have a positive influence on the lungs, heart and circulatory system, exercise must raise the heart rate (or pulse) up to at least 120 beats per minute and hold it at that level for longer than 12 minutes. There are only a few activities which can be maintained with some degree of comfort for long enough periods to offer such a training effect (i.e., an aerobic effect). In no particular order, these are running, swimming, cycling and rowing. Some activities like tennis, handball, squash and a few others *can* be aerobic, but often are not.

There are two possible answers to the question of how to combine aerobic sessions with weight training. The first of these

Running is one of the best forms of endurance exercise when the pace is slow enough to allow for conversation with a partner.

is to alternate aerobic days with weight days. This way one can do fairly heavy sessions daily, but with the dual advantages of variety and having a program that produces both strength and cardio-respiratory fitness. The second and perhaps better alternative is to do daily aerobic workouts and supplement them three times a week with light weight sessions. In this case, emphasis is placed on aerobic conditioning and the strength training merely fortifies this fitness. When combining aerobics and weight training, my experience has shown that it is usually a better idea to weight train before running, swimming, etc. There are some rare individuals who will have enough discipline to do a progressive resistance workout after charging up and down hills for an hour or two, but unfortunately most will skip the weights under such circumstances.

A few of you might be doubting the value of added strength. To my mind, strength acts as insurance against the pitfalls of everyday life. You never know when extra neck and upper back strength might prevent whiplash in a car wreck, or when one might need whole body power to fend off a mugger. And if these arguments don't convince you, I'll personally guarantee that weight workouts will make you into a better bowler, golfer or whatever your sport happens to be.

It is relatively difficult, but not impossible, to train aerobically with weights. In a minute I'll outline such a program, but first let me give you a few sample programs that can be combined with aerobic workouts of other sorts. Here is an easy one employing barbells and dumbbells:

Exercise	Sets	Reps	Men	Women
1. Clean and Press	1	12-15	35%	25%
2. Half Squat	2	12-15	80%	70%
3. Bench Press	2	8-12	40%	30%
4. Bent Rowing (Dumbbell)	2	8-12	40%	30%
5. Military Press	1	8-12	35%	25%
6. Barbell Curl	1	8-12	30%	20%
7. Situps	1	25-50	---	---

And here is another easy one, this time done exclusively on a Universal Gym:

Exercise	Sets	Reps	Men	Women
1. Leg Press	2	15-20	100%	80%
2. Bench Press	2	8-12	40%	30%
3. Lat Pulldown	2	12-15	40%	30%
4. Seated Press	2	8-12	35%	25%
5. Pulley Curl	1	8-12	30%	20%
6. Lat Pressdown	1	8-12	25%	15%
7. Leg Raise	1	25-100	---	---

Both of these schedules are of the type that can be done on the same day as a heavy aerobic workout. Neither should take more than 15 minutes to complete.

For a schedule that can be alternated with aerobic sessions (aerobics one day, weight training the next), try this heavier barbell and dumbbell routine:

Exercise	Sets	Reps	Men	Women
1. Clean and Press	1	12-15	35%	25%
2. Bench Squat	3	12-15	80%	70%
3. Leg Curl	2	12-15	20%	15%
4. Calf Raise	3-5	20-30	100%	80%
5. Bent Row	3	9-12	40%	30%
6. Shrug	2	12-15	50%	40%
7. Stiff-Leg Deadlift	1	9-12	40%	30%
8. Bench Press	3-5	8-10	40%	30%
9. Standing Laterals	3	12-15	10%	5%
10. Dumbbell Curls	3	8-12	30%	20%
11. Dumbbell French Press	3	8-12	30%	20%
12. Wrist Curls	3-5	12-25	30%	20%
13. Sidebend	1-3	25-100	---	---
14. Situps	1-3	25-50	---	---

And here's a heavy type of Universal Gym workout:

Exercise	Sets	Reps	Men	Women
1. Leg Press	3-5	15-20	100%	80%
2. Leg Extension	3	15-20	40%	30%
3. Leg Curl	3	15-20	20%	15%
4. Calf Press	3-5	20-30	100%	80%
5. Lat Pulldown	3	12-15	40%	30%

6. Seated Row	3	12-15	40%	30%
7. Bench Press	3-5	8-12	40%	30%
8. Seated Press	3	8-12	35%	25%
9. Pulley Curl	3	8-12	30%	20%
10. Lat Pressdown	3	8-12	25%	15%
11. Situps	1	25-100	---	---

The only weight training avenue toward aerobic fitness is circuit training. This technique is fully discussed in the next chapter, but to describe it briefly here, it amounts to doing series of exercises with little or no rest between each movement. Here is an example of that type of program (another program of this type is given in the next chapter):

Series I

1. Half Squat
2. Situps
3. Shrug
4. Bench Press
5. Barbell Curl
6. Calf Machine

Series II

1. Leg Curl
2. Dumbbell Curl
3. Incline Dumbbell Press
4. Lat Pulldown
5. Side Laterals
6. Leg Raises

Series III

1. Leg Press
2. Calf Press
3. Stiff-Leg Deadlift
4. Incline Curls
5. Parallel Bar Dips
6. Incline French Press

Series IV

1. Twisting Movement
2. Leg Extension
3. Bent-Arm Pullover
4. Seated Pulley Row
5. Lat Pressdown
6. Upright Rowing

Anything between one and three sets of each exercise should keep your pulse rate up for *at least* 12 minutes. I would recommend reps of eight to 20, and you should average at least one set per minute of exercise time. Such circuit training workouts can be used very profitably as a substitute for an outdoor workout when one is becoming stale or when the weather is bad.

Physical Self-Improvement

For many individuals, weight training has a cosmetic value

in helping to build up or reduce areas of the body that are not quite up to par. Building up an underdeveloped bodypart is relatively easy. All one needs to do is look in the exercise pool in Chapter Three, pick anywhere between one and five exercises, and consistently work at these exercises three times a week for five to 12 sets each workout. This will give men muscle and women curves. It's just that simple.

Women, however, do have several additional considerations regarding figure control and development. First, it is very difficult to lose weight in a specific body area without dieting to remove fat. Along the same lines, physicians and physiologists scoff at the existence of cellulites which supposedly cause fat wrinkles in the hips and upper thighs. Such wrinkles are actually caused by two things – too much body fat and too little muscle tone in thighs and hips, or in any other area for that matter. I have seen dramatic cases where such fat wrinkles were eliminated by only one or two exercise sessions. And this was entirely the result of improved muscle tone. Thus a combination of both diet and exercise will yield the best results when one desires to lose weight in some area of the body.

Building up a body area is merely a matter of increasing muscle volume. Skinny female legs can be built up to the point of alluring curves over a period of time–for example, by doing squats, calf presses, leg curls and leg extensions. This technique will also work for arms, but unfortunately will do little to increase bust size. Breast tissue is fatty and has muscle only in the underlying pectorals. Some very small amount of size increase can be expected by enlarging the pectorals via bench presses and lying laterals, but women should be forewarned that this is a very long process.

Feelin' Good

In recent years a sizeable number of people have been training with weights simply because it feels good and they enjoy it. You can train outdoors in good weather, or indoors when nobody in his right mind goes outside. And there just seems to be something very relaxing about eroding away the day's tension and cares with a few sets of bench presses, squats or curls. Give it a try and you'll see what I mean.

7

Advanced Training Techniques

All of the preceding chapters, with their many routines for each activity, have limitations in that most of the schedules are suitable only for a four- to six-month period at best. At that point a person graduates into the advanced category and can begin making up his or her own training routines by using the information we'll include in this chapter.

Organizing Your Own Routine

For a few months you will be able to change the basic routine around sufficiently to keep it interesting by simply substituting one exercise for another that works the same bodypart. You can look in the exercise pool chapter for possible substitutions. It could be as simple as changing from barbell bench presses to dumbbell bench presses, or from presses behind the neck to presses in front. Later, more sophisticated changes can be introduced, such as substituting bent-over rowing for lat pulldowns in order to strengthen the *latissimus dorsi* muscles of the mid-back.

In my experience, it is almost obligatory to modify training schedules every four to six weeks. Due to the monotonous nature of weight training, it is easy to grow both mentally and physically fatigued by staying on the same weight routine for months at a time.

The most important consideration in organizing your own training program is to include exercises for each bodypart, with special emphasis on those areas which have key significance for you. More than one exercise can be included for these muscle groups in an effort to work them harder.

Sequencing of exercises in a workout is another important consideration. Recent research has shown that bodyparts should be exercised in the following order:

1. Thighs
2. Back
3. Chest
4. Deltoids
5. Biceps-Triceps
6. Forearms
7. Abdominals
8. Neck-Calves

The above sequencing goes from the largest to the smallest muscle groups, and to a slightly lesser extent, from the most important muscles for the majority of individuals to the least vital. Since one has only a limited amount of energy to expend at weight training, many individuals are unable to sustain a high energy level and are forced to cut short some heavy workouts. If this is the case, it just stands to reason that available energy should be expended on the more important muscle groups.

The above tips on sequencing are nice to follow, but it's not vital to do so. Indeed, most experienced trainees do not subscribe in practice to such "ideal" workout schemes. One hard-and-fast rule in sequencing must be observed, however. It is essential to always train the biceps after back and triceps after chest and shoulders. The reason for this lies in the balance of strength between various muscle groups. The deltoids and pectorals, for example, are much stronger than the triceps at the backs of your upper arms. As a result of this imbalance, the triceps will give out from fatigue while doing bench presses long before the pectorals and deltoids have been exercised to their fullest potential.

From the preceding discussion, it should be obvious that back muscles are seldom thoroughly exercised because the biceps give out too soon, while the pectorals and deltoids suffer the same fate because of relatively weak triceps. Now we come to the reason for exercising arms last. If biceps are already tired from curls, they will fail even sooner when doing lat machine pulldowns, magnifying even more the degree to which the lats are under-exercised. Thus, the only way to make the best of a bad situation is by working the arms last.

The Principle of Pre-Exhaustion

There is one way to overcome weak muscle groups and thoroughly exercise deltoids, lats and pectorals. This method is also applicable to thighs, which cannot be worked adequately with squats due to the lower back being a bit weaker than your thighs. To exercise big muscle groups to maximum potential, it becomes necessary to do a pre-exhaustion set before a heavy movement for that area. This pre-exhaustion set works the big muscle group *without* arm involvement and it is immediately followed by the very heavy movement *with* arms involved. Here are five combinations that you might try using pre-exhaustion procedures (remember, *no* rest between sets):

Chest—Bent-Arm Laterals and Bench Presses.

Upper Back — Shoulder Shrugs and Upright Rows.

Lats—Bent-Arm Pullovers and Lat Pulldowns.

Deltoids — Standing Laterals and Press Behind Neck.

Thighs — Leg Press, Leg Extension and Squat.

For maximum effect, proceed with each exercise until failure, or until no more repetitions can be done. I have often done one set each of the thigh workout with weights that allow between 15 and 20 reps per exercise, and I can attest that this schedule is intense enough to be equal to 10 to 15 sets of heavy squats! And the advantage of pre-exhaustion is that it's a tremendous timesaver.

Gaining Weight

A large number of individuals turn to weight training in

order to gain weight. Weight training is especially popular with male athletes who need to add body bulk for football, track and field weight events, or for other activities in which additional muscle mass will come in handy. There are also many women who require or want more bodyweight. For the benefit of this latter group, we should point out that all suggestions here apply to women as well as to men.

Of course, almost anyone can gain weight by becoming fat. Just eat a gallon of ice cream each day along with a few pounds of rice, potatoes or bread. But what good is added fat? What you need to do is to add plenty of muscle with as little fat as possible, because only muscle is functional. That's the trick, therefore—how does an athlete go about adding muscular bodyweight? And how does he or she do it quickly?

I have personally witnessed many football players gain 20 to 30 pounds of solid muscular weight over the course of a three-month summer of heavy exercise. Note that I said *heavy* exercise. Doing this type of work combined with a very heavy intake of protein food is the secret to adding muscle bulk. A good weight gaining program includes a few basic exercises done with very heavy weights, low reps and a high number of sets. Here is a sample routine for gaining weight:

1. Squat: 1 set, 15 reps (warmup); 5 sets, 6-8 reps
2. Bench Press: 1 set, 15 reps; 5 sets, 4-6 reps
3. Bent Rowing: 1 set, 15 reps; 5 sets, 6-8 reps
4. Bent-Arm Pullover: 3 sets, 12-15 reps
5. Press Behind Neck: 3 sets, 6-8 reps
6. Barbell Curl: 3 sets, 6-8 reps
7. Stiff-Leg Deadlift: 3 sets, 12-15 reps
8. Situps: 1 set, 15-20 reps (with extra resistance)

If this program seems short, don't be fooled by it. This is all the exercise necessary. Should you feel like you need more training at the end of this workout, it should be a signal that you really need to use heavier poundages. Added muscle size is contingent on using greater and greater weights, so add poundage to the bar as often as possible instead of more exercises or sets.

Avoid doing more than one set of abdominal exercises per training session, as more than one set will slow down weight gains. Several theories have been proposed on this subject, the most prominent being that a lot of situps or leg raises numb the solar plexus, one of the body's major nerve centers. This may be true, but no proof exists. I have, however, observed the relationship between excessive abdominal work and slow bodyweight gains much too often to ignore the phenomenon.

The "gain-weight" diet is liable to break your bank account in about two shakes. It must be very rich in expensive protein foods, but also fairly high in fats and carbohydrates. Try to strike an approximate balance of 60 percent protein, 25 percent carbohydrates and 15 percent unsaturated fats on a caloric basis. Proteins include meat, fish, poultry, milk products, eggs, nuts, beans and peas. Carbohydrates should come from natural sources like milk, whole grain products, potatoes and honey, while the best sources of fats are nuts and unsaturated vegetable oils which can be used in cooking.

A good axiom for weight gainers is to never allow oneself to get hungry. Eat three or four substantial meals each day and snack constantly on protein foods between meals. Good snacks include cheese, cold cuts, hard-boiled eggs, yogurt or milkshakes made with milk and commercial protein powder. You can take all of the other food supplements you like, but be sure to include a B-Complex tablet with each meal. B-Complex helps to increase the appetite and influence weight gains.

Bodyweight Reduction

Many individuals need to lose weight if they desire to approach their athletic potential. The proper combination of diet, weight training and specialized workouts can result in very rapid weight losses. I have seen many men lose six to eight pounds in one week, many women five or six.

Basically, if you take in more calories than your body can use up, the excess is stored as fat somewhere in the body.

From this it should be apparent that you must, in order to reduce, either consume fewer calories, use up more calories, or a combination of these two. The best way, by far, of losing weight has proven to be a combination of sensible diet and intense exercise.

The best reduction diet I have observed is a high protein and very low carbohydrate regimen. Eat all you want of meats, fish, eggs, cheese and poultry. Eat whenever you are hungry, but only proteins. Drink only water or sugarless diet sodas. Under no circumstances should you eat anything with sugar or flour in it. Using a vitamin-mineral supplement is good insurance against possible vitamin deficiencies from excluding fruits and vegetables, as only one salad per day with oil and vinegar dressing is allowed. It is also a good idea to consult a physician whenever embarking on any type of diet.

Workouts should be aimed at using up plenty of calories. At first this will be tough because the initial two or three diet days will leave you with low energy. The body soon adjusts, however, and energy levels will quickly climb, at which time workouts can be stepped up. In using weight training to help lose weight, you should aim to do higher reps and train faster. When exercised, big muscle groups will burn up more calories than smaller ones. You might also weight train every day instead of the usual three times weekly.

In summary, consistency is the real key to losing weight. It takes daily high-caloric expenditure type workouts, as well as consistent adherence to a diet. Once a trend of weight loss has been established, you can start including one "junk day" each week during which you can eat *anything*. Even eight or 10 hot fudge sundaes once a week can't do you any harm once you establish a loss pattern, so eat up!

Gaining Strength Without Bulk

In the two previous sections, we covered gaining and losing weight, but what about the person who wants strength without any added bodyweight? In most cases this can be accomplished by training with very low repetitions, usually a series of single efforts. First decide what area you want to strengthen and choose one exercise for that group. Try to go with heavy basic movements like bench presses for chest, squats for thighs, bent rowing for upper back, etc. Next test yourself and find out your limit for each exercise. Finally follow this set and rep scheme for each movement:

1 set, 5 reps, 60% of maximum
1 set, 3 reps, 75%
1 set, 1 rep, 85%
5 sets, 1 rep, 95%

As soon as you can do five singles at 95 percent, increase the weight for each set by five or 10 pounds. I have seen male athletes increase strength at a rate of five percent per week for several months on this type of schedule without bodyweight gains. Women can expect equal strength gains and also no bodyweight increase.

Repetition Schemes

As mentioned in an earlier chapter, low repetitions will build strength, high reps endurance, and middle-range reps a combination of the two. That's fine as far as it goes, but there are many rep schemes which are not included in this basic breakdown.

The simplest method of using reps is to do multiple sets of the same number of repetitions with the same weight. This is the old three-sets-of-10-with-70-pounds idea that many use today. If you are working very hard on every set, however, chances are you'll get the 10 reps on the first set, eight on the second and maybe seven on the third. As long as you are working as hard as possible, don't worry about the rep drop. Or if you feel compelled to keep the reps up, you can drop the weight with each set.

Many competitive weightlifters prefer to use a set number of reps (two, three or five usually) and then work up in jumps of 15 to 20 pounds through several sets. This makes many of the buildup sets become non-maximum efforts and mere warmups for that penultimate set or two that socks in real strength.

Another strength builder is the pyramid system of raising the weight and lowering the reps with each set. The classic example of this is a 5-4-3-2-1 rep scheme, but I have had great success with many athletes using a 12-10-8-6-4-2 scheme. Carrying it all a step further, you can, for an extra super workout every two or three weeks, work back down again by lowering the weight and raising the reps, e.g., 5-4-3-2-1-2-3-4-5.

Machines vs. Free Weights

Athletes must have tremendous motor control to be successful in any sport. This is the basic reason why I always recommend the use of free weights if a choice exists between such equipment and weight training machines. These machines exercise muscle groups along a set arc and relieve an individual of the onus of controlling the weight. Free weights, on the other hand, demand constant control and balance, two factors that I believe have good carry-over value for athletes.

Daily Workouts?

A person can profit from *daily* weight training under two conditions. The first of these occurs when an experienced trainee wants to break out of a slump in which strength gains have not been forthcoming. In this case I would recommend one or two weeks of five or six weekly workouts for the same bodypart. Try one day of 8-10 reps, one of 5-6, one of 2-3, and then start the cycle all over again. Usually a week or so of this training will cause a quick quantum jump in strength, after which regular workouts can be resumed.

The second way to train daily is called a split routine. It consists of dividing the body into two or three segments and working each segment on alternate days. Each bodypart will have at least one day of rest while some other section is receiving the brunt of a workout. The classic split routine is upper body-lower body. Here's an example:

Mon-Wed-Fri (or Mon-Thurs)	Tues-Thurs-Sat (or Tues-Fri)
Chest	Legs
Arms	Lower Back

Shoulders   Abdominals
Upper Back

Here are a couple of other ways to split up your routine for more than three workouts a week:

Mon-Wed-Fri   Tues-Thurs-Sat

Deltoids   Biceps
Triceps   Back
Chest   Legs
Abdominals

Or. . .

Mon-Thurs   Tues-Fri   Wed-Sat

Arms   Chest   Legs
Shoulders   Back   Abdominals

The primary advantage of the split routine is that it will allow you more time to work each bodypart, mainly because you are training fewer bodyparts per workout. This, of course, allows you to train harder and more thoroughly. The end result of such harder training is usually faster strength gains.

Circuit Training

As mentioned previously, it is difficult to attain any significant degree of cardio-respiratory fitness through weight training. The one method which will result in varying degrees of such fitness (depending on how hard you push it) is called circuit training. This involves choosing 10 to 15 exercises and setting up stations for each around the training area. Movements should be chosen for each part of the body and stations should be arranged so that no bodypart is trained at two stations consecutively. An example of a training circuit is on page 194.

The object is to move rapidly from one station to another with no rest between exercises. This will very quickly accelerate the pulse and cause an oxygen debt. Training with no rest is relatively easy if the same bodypart is not trained at consecutive stations, because each part can rest while another works. This

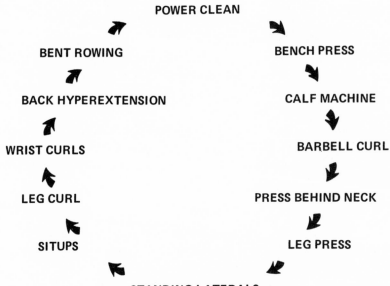

Circuit training builds endurance.

does present a significant stimulation to core endurance, and if such training is kept up for at least 15 minutes, an improvement will result in cardio-respiratory efficiency. This 15-plus minutes should mean two or three trips through a circuit like the one presented.

A second type of circuit training program utilizes short series of five or six movements each. Again, exercises should be chosen so only one per bodypart is included in each series. Run through each series with no rest, take a break of about one minute after each series, and repeat each series two or three times. Here is an example of such a short series workout:

Series I	Series II
1. Leg Press	1. Leg Extension
2. Situps	2. Shoulder Shrug
3. Bench Press	3. Barbell Curl
4. Wrist Curl	4. Side Bend
5. Lat Machine Pulldown	5. Calf Press

Series III	Series IV
1. Press Behind Neck	1. Upright Rowing
2. Twisting Movement	2. Seated Calf Exercise
3. Leg Curl	3. Parallel Bar Dips
4. Incline Press	4. Dumbbell Curls
5. Seated Rowing	5. Leg Raises

Push here also for a very breathless condition. If you don't get to this point with either the short series or the longer circuit program, either speed up your training or use heavier exercise poundages, preferably the former.

Peaking

Athletes in all sports currently modify their training in the weeks before a major competition in order to reach a peak of skill and condition. Weight training can also be adjusted to attain such a peak. It is done differently, however, for endurance events than for strength-oriented sports.

Endurance athletes should begin weight training at least six months before the major competition. At that point strength building is stressed by using relatively heavy weights and rests of a minute or two between sets. With every few weeks, rest periods should be shortened between sets. The goal for the last three or four weeks is to achieve a circuit program with absolutely zero rest between sets. Of course, as rests become shorter, it will be necessary to slowly diminish the resistance used. This does not, however, mean that you will be losing strength, since the intensity will still be very high.

Strength athletes should also increase the intensity of their training while peaking, but in a different way. Six months before, the athlete might be training with heavy weights and reps of about five per set. Then the weights are gradually raised and the reps progressively lowered as one comes close to the meet. Finally, many workouts will stress quick performance of sets and single reps, while a few other workouts will involve sets of two or three reps. The point is, however, that for strength peaks the weights increase as the reps go progressively down.

Endurance intensity, on the other hand, results from shortening rests.

Tapering Off

Regardless of what peaking method you use, it is essential to taper off training during the final week to 10 days before a big competition. It would be senseless for a record high jumper, for example, to enter a meet with his/her legs still loggy from a heavy squat workout the day before. The last heavy workout should be taken seven to 10 days prior to your meet. Then two workouts of gradually lesser intensity should be taken, with a final very light and fast session of 12 to 15 sets. This final workout should take place three days before your meet. With two full days of rest, the body will recuperate completely from the weight workouts, but will still retain maximum strength. After more than two days off, however, strength will begin to decrease.

Overtraining

Sometimes a very fine line exists between doing enough work for maximum speed gains and doing too much. When one does workouts of excessive length, it's possible to overtrain and become stale. You can tell if you're overtraining when you exhibit one or more of the following symptoms:

1. Chronic fatigue.
2. Sleeplessness.
3. Loss of appetite.
4. Lack of enthusiasm for workouts.
5. Slow recovery from previous workouts.
6. Increase in morning pulse rate.

There are several ways to overcome staleness from overtraining. The easiest is to take a week or so off from workouts and then when you start up again, change your schedule to inject new variety into training. Getting a training partner will also increase interest in training and overcome staleness.

Taking precautionary measures is the best cure for overtraining. This can be done most easily by changing exercise programs each four to six weeks in order to avoid boredom. Other precautionary measures include obtaining sufficient sleep and rest, as well as maintenance of a quality diet.

Power Rack Training

With the coming of the isometric fad several years ago, workouts employing a power rack became popular. This type of exercise has lost its popularity in recent years, but does have some value for building strength. Here is an illustration of power rack training:

Ray Leso does military presses on the power rack. Note the use of a lifting belt.

This type of workout involves limited movement with very heavy weights. Only small segments of each basic exercise are performed. Let's take the bench press as an example. You can set the lower power rack pins to hold the bar at chest level and the upper pins about six inches higher. Then bench press a very heavy weight three to five reps along this six-inch range, holding the last repetition for at least 12 seconds against the top pins before training. Then the pins should be set for the middle range and finally for the last six inches of the lift. Of course, this same procedure can be applied to many other basic movements.

Nautilus Training

In recent years, Nautilus training machines have become popular. Such machines have a pulley that allows for balanced and variable resistance over a long range of motion. Extravagant claims have been made for these machines, but my own experiments for the past three years with Nautilus apparatus have failed to verify such claims. In addition, these machines are *very* expensive. In the event you ever run across one, here's how you'll recognize it:

The Nautilus pull-over machine is characterized by its snail-shaped spiral cam.

Record Keeping

A large number of athletes in other sports keep detailed training diaries. This is also a wise idea in weight training, as improvements in strength can be seen more easily over a long haul than from workout to workout. In fact, if I had a dollar for every time I got a training boost by looking at my diary to trace improvement, I could retire in Hawaii.

Any format for this diary is suitable as long as the trainee can read it. I'll show you a system fairly standardized in weight training circles. If you do a set of barbell curls, 10 reps with 120 pounds, it should look like this in your book:

1. Barbell Curl: 120X10

Your book could also read 120X10X10X10, or three sets of 10 with that weight. Or, it could be 120X10; 130X8; 140X6, which means 120 ten times, a second set of eight with 130 pounds and a third of six reps with 140. Of course, this scheme will work with any movement and each exercise should be listed, one below another, down the pages of your diary.

Pushing

As my final comment, I must stress the great importance of increasing training poundages. Strength gains are absolutely dependent on increasing training poundages at regular intervals. It's not easy sometimes; often it will take a lot of willpower to up the training load. But keep on pushing and the strength will come. And with strength will come better sports performance and improved health. That's what it's all about, isn't it?

APPENDIX
and
ANNOTATED
BIBLIOGRAPHY

APPENDIX

ANATOMY OF AN ADJUSTABLE BARBELL AND DUMBBELL SET

BARBELL

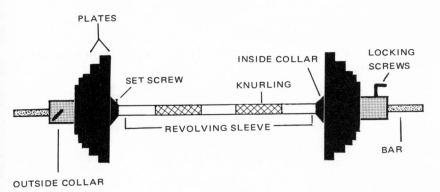

PLATES

INSIDE COLLAR

LOCKING SCREWS

SET SCREW

KNURLING

REVOLVING SLEEVE

BAR

OUTSIDE COLLAR

DUMBBELL

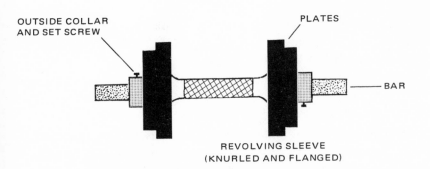

OUTSIDE COLLAR AND SET SCREW

PLATES

BAR

REVOLVING SLEEVE
(KNURLED AND FLANGED)

WRENCH

(USED TO TIGHTEN SET SCREWS)

ANNOTATED BIBLIOGRAPHY

Periodicals

Health & Strength, Monthly issue, subscription $10.00/year from Health & Strength Publishing Co. Ltd., Halton House, 20-23 Holborn, London E.C. 1, UK.

> Covers all phases of weight training. Particularly strong on articles for women and news of the annual NABBA Mr. Universe contest. Edited by Oscar Heidenstam.

Iron Man, bimonthly issue, subscription $5.00/year ($9.00/2 years) from Iron Man Publishing Company, 512 Black Hills Avenue, Alliance Nebraska 69301.

> Excellent coverage of bodybuilding, weightlifting and powerlifting. Considered by the weight training elite to be the least biased of all American publications. Edited by Peary Rader.

Muscle Builder/Power, monthly issue, subscription $10.00/year from Muscle Builder Publications, Inc., 21100 Erwin Street, Woodland Hills, California 91364.

> Very heavy concentration on advanced bodybuilders. The Official IFBB organ. Strong commercial bias in virtually all articles. Edited by Gene Mozee.

Muscle Mag International, quarterly issue (with plans to expand to monthly), subscription $5.00/year from Health Culture, Subscription Department, 270 Rutherford Road South, Brampton, Ontario, Canada L6W 3K7.

> A new magazine on the scene concentrating on all phases of bodybuilding. The editorial policy is to run articles appealing to the general public more than to hard core bodybuilders. Edited by Robert Kennedy.

Muscle Training Illustrated, bi-monthly, subscription $6.00/ year ($10.00/2 years) from Muscle Man, Inc., 1664 Utica Avenue, Brooklyn, New York 11234.

> Caters almost exclusively to contest bodybuilders. Fairly strong commercial slant to most material. Edited by Dan Lurie.

Muscular Development, bi-monthly, subscription $4.00/year ($7.50/2 years or $7.50 for one year of both Muscular Development and Strength & Health) from Muscular Development, P.O. Box 1707, York, Pennsylvania 17405.

> Covers powerlifting and bodybuilding, usually with several authoritative articles on each subject. Occasional commercial slant to articles. Edited by John C. Grimek.

Powerman, bimonthly issue, subscription $5.00/year ($9.00/2 years) from Powerman Magazine, P.O. Box 3005, Erie, Pennsylvania 16508.

> Devoted exclusively to the sport of powerlifting. Plenty of photos, contest results and training advice articles.

Strength & Health, bi-monthly, subscriptions same as for Muscular Development from Strength & Health, P.O. Box 1707, York, Pennsylvania 17405.

> Emphasis on Olympic style weightlifting and family fitness through weight training and proper nutrition. Carries women's articles and occasional profiles of famous athletes who train with weights.

Books

Ditillo, Anthony, **Development of Bulk & Power** (Alliance, Nebraska: Iron Man Publishing Co., 1974).

A $6.00 hard bound book with philosophy, exercises and nutrition necessary to add bodyweight and gain strength.

Fallon, Michael and Jim Saunders, **Muscle Building** (New York: Arco Books, various editions).

Recommended book for beginners and advanced men. In cludes both photos and line drawings.

Franz, Edward, **Beginning Weight Training** (Belmont, California: Wadsworth Publishing Company, Inc., 1969).

Good paperback, costs a bit over $1.00, plenty of basic advice and line drawings.

Gaines, Charles and George Butler, **Pumping Iron** (Simon & Schuster, 1975).

A 222 page ($6.95) paperbound book with 100 photos on the sport of bodybuilding. Recommended for novices, advanced men, or anyone interested in the sport.

Gironda, Vince, **Blueprint For The Bodybuilder**, $3.00 from Gironda, 11262 Ventrua Blvd., North Hollywood, CA 91604.

A small nutritional manual aimed at advanced bodybuilders. Gironda has produced many great champions.

Health Culture, **Abdominal Course**, $3.98 from Health Culture, P.O. Box 2009, Brampton, Ontario, Canada L6T 3S3.

Complete abdominal course covering exercises, diets, supplements.

Heidenstam, Oscar, **Modern Bodybuilding**, (Buchanan, New York: Emerson Books, Inc.)

Comprehensive guide to fitness and bodybuilding by Britain's greatest authority. Fully illustrated by 134 line drawings and 12 photographs.

Hoffman, Bob, **York Abdominal Course,** $1.00 from Bob Hoffman, Box 1707, York, PA 17405.

> A million seller over the past 20 odd years. Complete set of stomach exercises.

Kirkley, George, **Weight Lifting and Weight Training** (New York: Arco).

> Low Priced and superior paperback. Photos and drawings. Recommended.

Knipp, Russ, **Olympic Weightlifting Manual—Technical Training Simplified,** $5.00 from Russ Knipp, AIA Arrowhead Springs, San Bernardino, CA 92414.

> Advice for advanced weightlifters from a several times US national champion and world record holder. Over 170 clear photos illustrating advanced techniques.

Mann, Stan K., **Business Is Great** (Alliance, Nebraska: Iron Man Publishing Co.)

> Hardbound 148 page manual on successful operation of private commercial gyms. Outlines courses, business techniques, diets. Essential for anyone who wants to open a health club.

Mozee, Gene, **You Can Build 20" Arms,** $5.00 from Mozee, 3969 D. 3rd Ave., Los Angeles, CA 90008.

> Covers complete arm development including ten routines, step by step instructions, diets and exercises.

Murray, Jim and Peter V. Karpovich, **Weight Training in Athletics** (Englewood Cliffs, New Jersey: Prentice-Hall, 1956).

> Fair treatment of the subject with photos and drawings, but is outdated.

Pearl, Bill, Three Courses (**Building Bulk and Power,** $4.00; **Build Big Arms,** $3.00; **Fabulous Forearms,** $2.00) from Pearl, 1210 East Green Street, Pasadena, CA 91106.

> Training advice from a treble Mr. Universe winner and one of the greatest bodybuilders of all time.

Rader, Peary, **The Rader Master Bodybuilding & Weight Gaining**

Course, $5.00 from Iron Man Publishing Company.

Courses writen by *Iron Man* magazine editor Peary Rader. Includes wall chart to illustrate exercises.

Randall, Bruce, **The Barbell Way To Physical Fitness,** $7.95 from Book List, Unit 1, 270 Rutherford Road, Brampton, Ontario, Canada L6W 3K7.

Comprehensive 148 page, 190 photograph book written by a former Mr. Universe who once reduced his bodyweight from 401 lbs. to 185.

Ravelle, Lou, **Bodybuilding For Everyone** (Buchanan, New York: Emerson Books).

A book for the average man or woman trying to get into shape. Illustrated with drawings and photos.

Richford, Carl, Four Courses (**The Principles of Successful Bodybuilding; Lower Body Training & Posing Hints: Upper Body Training; Modern Nutrition for Bodybuilders**), $3.00 each from Iron Man Publishing Company.

Four courses aimed at the advanced bodybuilder. All are illustrated and authoritive.

Salvati, Michael, **The Production of Muscular Bulk,** $4.95 from Iron Man Publishing Company.

A complete guide to gaining weight. Over 100 pages and includes exercises and diets.

Schwarzenegger, Arnold, Ten Courses (**Developing A Mr. Universe Body; The Art of Posing**—$2.00 each—**Build Massive Arms; Building A Giant 60-inch Chest; Building Doorway-Wide Shoulders; Building The Legs Of An Oak; Build Massive Size/Gain Muscular Weight; Huge Muscular Mass/Razor Sharp Definition; The Arnold Album; Building A Wide, Powerful Back**—$3.00 each or $20.00 for all ten courses) from Arnold Strong, Box 1234, Santa Monica CA 90406.

Very well illustrated courses by the greatest bodybuilder of all time, winner of 5 Mr. Universe and 6 Mr. Olympia titles.

Scott, Larry, Eleven Courses (**Building A Mr. America Chest; Developing That V-Man Taper; Herculean Thighs; Cannonball Delts; My Photo Album; Instinctive Training; Art of Posing—** all $2.00 each—**How I Built 20 Inch Arms; Molding The Mr. America Body; How to Slice Up Your Physyique; Secrets of Bulking**—$3.00 each; special all eleven for $15.00) from Scott, Box 21096, Salt Lake City, Utah 84121.

> Courses from the first Mr. Olympia and one of the all-time great bodybuilders.

Steiner, Bradly J., **A Complete Guide To Effective Barbell Training** (Alliance, Nebraska: Iron Man Publishing Co., 1975).

> Good basic information on getting started in weight training. Cloth bound, 112 pages with plenty of clear photos illustrating the various techniques.

Webster, Dave, **How To Clean & Jerk**, $2.00 from Iron Man Publishing Company.

> A superior 40 page treatise on techniques of executing the clean and jerk by the Scottish National Coach. Illustrated by fine photos and drawings.

Webster, Dave, **The Two Hands Snatch**, $1.50 from Iron Man Publishing Company.

> Same as above, but covering snatch movement.

Weider, Joe, **The Weider System**, $10.00 from Weider Health and Fitness, 21100 Erwin Street, Woodland Hills CA 91364.

> Course and seven wall charts. Intended for beginning bodybuilders with plenty of ambition.

Weider, Joe, Three Powerlift Courses (**Deadlift: Bench Press; Squat**) each $2.98 from IFBB Headquarters, Weider Bldg., 2875 Bates Rd., Montreal, P.Q. Canada H3S 1B7.

> Basic treatment of the powerlifts, including techniques and assistance exercises.

Zane, Frank, Four Courses (**How To Build Championship Legs And a Small Waistline: Total Training For The Total Body**— each $3.00—**Develop A Classic Muscular Upper Body**—$4.00—

Secrets of Advanced Bodybuilding–$5.00; or all four courses for $10.00) from Zane, Box 366, Santa Monica CA 90406.

Courses including diets from Mr. America, Mr. World, Mr. Universe. Recommended for novices and advanced men alike.

A catalog listing more than 1500 sports books is free for the asking from World Publications, Box 366, Mountain View, CA 94040.

INDEX

About the Author

Bill Reynolds has written more than 100 weight training and related articles in such diverse magazines as *Strength & Health, Runner's World, Muscular Development, Down River, Muscle Mag International, Nordic World, Iron Man, Aquatic World* and *Muscle Mag International.* Bill is so enthusiastic about the benefits of weight training for everyone's body that he donates his time several days a month to give lectures and clinics in the activity (see photo).

Bill's academic background (he's closing in on his Ph.D.) has contributed a great deal to his appreaciation of weight training, particularly for women. During a two-year stint as a graduate student at the University of Washington, Bill noticed increasing numbers of women enrolling in his weight training activity classes. The same trend continued for three years at the University of California. Today the classes are beginning to approach an ideal 50-50 sex ratio.

Bill Reynolds has a diverse athletic background. He has noted a steady progression in athletic ability from the time he began training with weights. "During high school, I might have spent a couple months a year on weight training, but as time went on, the workouts became more regular. The more I weight trained, the closer I came to realizing my potential as an athlete."

In one year during his military service, Bill was All-Conference in football, basketball, and track and field. He has been a regional powerlifting champion and has to his credit an official 238-foot javelin throw.

His interest in athletics has led Bill to training athletes and teams, both on college and professional levels. Last year, for example, he made up successful programs for crew and water polo teams at the University of California.

Bill is 30, resides in Mountain View, California and works as an editor for World Publications.